THE GIRL GUIDE

Annual 1982

Edited by Fiona Lawson

Copyright © MCMLXXXI
by The Girl Guides Association.
All rights reserved throughout the world.
Published in Great Britain
by World International Publishing Limited.
A Pentos Company,
P.O. Box 111, Great Ducie Street,
Manchester M60 3BL.
Printed in Belgium.
SBN 7235 6623 2.

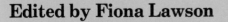

£2.50

GUIDING IN DENMARK

Hello! My name is Inga and I would like to tell you about Guiding in my country.

There are three main Associations in Denmark: the K.F.U.M. – Spejderne i Danmark (the Y.W.C.A. Scouts) which takes boys and is a church-based Association; the K.F.U.K. – Spejderne i Danmark (the Y.W.C.A. Girl Guides) and Det Danske Spejderkorps (The Danish Guide and Scout Association) for girls and boys, to which I belong.

I will tell you a little about my Association and its work. I am a leader for the Juniors aged 10-12, and also a Leader for the whole group. I live in a town called Rudkobing on Langeland, in the south of Denmark, (a little island connected by a bridge to Fyn.)

The girls and boys are divided into four age groups. The youngest are Micro-Guides/Scouts, aged 6-7 years. This is the newest age

Water activities during *Spejd-80*.

group to be added to our Association, and so there are only a few groups spread over the country at the moment. If we can get the leaders for this age group we hope it will expand in the near future.

The next age range is for girls and boys aged 8-10 years. They may choose to be called Cub Scouts, Brownies or Mini-Guides/Scouts. The childrens' Guide work is divided into theme groups: "Learning By Doing", "Out Into Nature", " We And The World", "Camplife",

"Help Yourself", "Help Others", "Sports", "Jack-Of-All-Trades", "Hobby". Within each group there are several badges that can be taken, and in the group the children plan which subjects they would like to work on.

Next we come to the Juniors, aged 10-12 years. They work on the same themes but to a more advanced stage, which is of course slightly more difficult. This age range has more practice in outdoor activities, walking, weekends away, and so on, and through these they experience some of the more exciting adventures Guiding/Scouting has to offer.

The 12-16 year olds are called Spejder (Guide), pronounced in English as 'spider'. They form Patrols, which can be for girls alone, for boys alone, or for mixed boys and girls. It is difficult to say which is best, as it very much depends upon the individual children and how they work together. The Patrols' programme ideas are to be found in booklets, each booklet containing three badges similar to those of the Juniors and Brownies /Cubs, but to a much more advanced stage. When the youngsters have taken

all three badges from a booklet they can call themselves a specialist.

Danish Guides and Scouts like hikes and other trips with the Patrol, and in that way they try to experience the life of the small group. From 15 years up to 23 years you can become a Seniorspejder (a Senior). As a senior you can choose your own particular subject. Many senior groups choose to work with a single theme over a long period of time. Many also help as assistants with the younger age group sections.

All the age groups form one large group, and this certainly helps in many areas to strengthen the community spirit. We can all go away for the weekend together, or have combined evenings, perhaps a camp fire. This can also be taken to International Level as in our big National camp called 'Spejd-80'. Many groups sent representatives from all age groups. Through these and other activities Scouts and Guides get a chance to experience what real international understanding is.

Summer camp is for most Guides and Scouts the highlight of the year. All around Denmark we have many activity centres, some administered by the Division or District area. Here they offer a wide variety of outdoor activities.

At Thorobund you can sail in large or small boats, go rowing, or paddle a canoe. Other centres offer the chance to do large scale pioneering, work with clay and leather, go for interesting hikes, and many other activities. Each centre has a staff team who help to arrange an interesting programme.

Some groups prefer to go by themselves and there are still friendly farmers who will let you use their fields for camping. When Danish Guides and Scouts go camping they often try to live as close to nature as possible. Equipment for such trips may only include a few tools, a tent,

Three members of the group, dressed for the weather.

some pots and pans, or maybe less than that. Some groups arrange their camps overseas, perhaps to visit a group with whom they have been corresponding.

Included in the Guiding/Scouting programme is a week in September, when all the associations in Denmark try to earn money by working, and this is called 'Spejderhjælpen'. The money goes into a common pool. Spejderhjælpen means 'healthy children help sick children', and the money is used all over the world. The Guides and Scouts pay a regular subscription, but if the group wishes to have special activities, for instance its own hut or camping place, they have to arrange some fund-raising activities. It could be a bazaar for which the Guides and Scouts may make articles themselves, or they may collect newspapers, as old newspapers are bought by some factories. Most groups work well with the parents of their members. Parents are often invited to take part in special family activities. The group committee has representatives from the parents included, together with the leaders.

My special responsibility is finance, and to some extent the training of the leaders. There are courses at local level, and also further afield in other parts of Denmark. Through a law in Denmark covering spare time

occupations, the government give economic help towards the training of leaders. They also help us to rent meeting rooms, huts and camping grounds. At local level, and at central level as well, co-operation frequently takes place between Guide and Scout Associations.

Many leaders are members of local groups for sparetime activities, and together with leaders from the other youth organisations try to plan some hobbies and activities for the children in their own areas. The Guide and Scout Associations in Denmark are very popular, and parents are keen for their children to join, so that the children can discover and enjoy friendship together with exciting adventure.

Inga

Spejderne i Danmark (the Y.W.C.A. Girl Guides) in camp and washing-up.

The surprising SANDWICH!

Pauline Viola of the London Danish Food Centre tells us all about Danish Open Sandwiches – and other things!

'Smorrebrod' is Denmark's national dish. The word means literally, 'buttered bread', but it is usually translated as Danish Open Sandwich – or 'Danwich' for short.

In Denmark there are two kinds of smorrebrod, called 'high' and 'low'. The first are made by specialists in hotels and restaurants; the 'low' are less elaborate and are made at home almost every day. The children take them to school; workers take them to the office or factory or to the fields, and even if you are at home, you eat them at lunchtime just the same.

In the past twenty years Danwiches, as we shall call them, have become very popular in Britain. At the Danish Food Centres in London, Manchester, Glasgow and Birmingham they are made with the authentic Danish foods and served in the traditional way, and in restaurants and department stores something very similar in appearance is often available. People are fascinated by their variety, the blending of flavours, the colourful and appetising appearance and, not least, by their delicious taste.

There is no culinary secret to making Danwiches. You can see all that goes into them at a glance, except the underlying piece of bread. Basically, they consist of a small piece of bread, well buttered, a generous topping, (replacing the filling of an English sandwich), and chosen garnishes.

Don't be too ambitious when you first begin to make Danwiches. You can make a delightful meal with one or two well-chosen varieties and two or three Danwiches should be sufficient for each person.

Obviously you will need Danish ingredients. A Danwich must be as Danish as possible or it may end up being no more than a sandwich without a top. Some of the best known cheeses to look for are Danish Blue, Havarti, Samsoe or Danbo. Then there are two kinds of butter in our shops, called Danelea and Lurpak, and of course most of us know Danish bacon with its famous stripmark. Having assembled all the ingredients – butter, bread, meats, cheese, vegetables, etc. study these four steps to successful Danwich making.

FOUR EASY RULES:

Cut the bread into ¼" thick slices about 2" × 4" – roughly half a slice from an ordinary small loaf.

Spread each piece with a good layer of Danish butter, making sure the bread is completely covered.

Arrange the topping (fish, meat, cheese, eggs, etc.) neatly on the buttered bread so that the base is hardly visible.

Decorate the topping with a selection of salads, mayonnaise, vegetables or fruit.

THE BREAD

The bread should be fresh with a good crust. Use white or brown bread or Danish ryebread, if available. Delicate flavours like mild cheese and chicken are best on white bread.

TOPPINGS

When Danwiches are to be eaten with a knife and fork, the topping should be of ample proportions to give a generous well-rounded look. Meats and certain types of cheese can sometimes be folded or rolled to add height, and often a piece of lettuce is tucked under one corner to give the topping a lift. Generally speaking one major ingredient – ham or cheese, for example – is used for the topping, which should always be regarded as the most important part of the Danwich in terms of quantity. When making Danwiches to pack up for a picnic or school lunchbox, the toppings are less generous.

GARNISHING

The garnishing adds a little crown of colour. Try to choose those which complement the flavour of the topping, using such items as lettuce, parsley, cress, radishes, tomato, cucumber, and even orange and lemon slices.

SERVING DISHES

Serve the finished Danwiches on a flat meat dish or tray. A cake server or palette knife is useful for lifting them onto the individual plates. You need a knife and fork to eat them.

PICNICKING WITH DANWICHES

When making Danwiches to pack up for a picnic or a school lunchbox, use rather less topping on each piece of bread and keep it and any garnish rather flat so that each piece can be wrapped in foil or film wrap and carried in a plastic box or bag. These 'low' Danwiches can be eaten in the fingers without a knife and fork or plate. Remember to pack a paper napkin in the box for sticky fingers!

ENTERTAINING WITH DANWICHES

Giving a Danish party is great fun. The food is gay and colourful and the Danwiches can be made in advance, covered with film and stored in the fridge until needed. Make as many varieties as you can manage and have a Danish cheese board to follow.

two easy-to-make ideas. They are especially good for a children's party.

Cheese Sputnik

Cut an orange so that it stands upright. Cut 3 ozs Samsoe cheese into cubes. Fix a cube of cheese and a piece of fruit or a nut onto ten cocktail sticks and push them a little way into the orange.

VIKING SHIP

To make the ship you will need a large banana, 3 ozs Danbo cheese cut into cubes, some grapes, cocktail sticks and a small paper sail. Slice the curved side of the banana to form a base. Put on the sail with a cocktail stick. Make up 5 sticks with a cheese cube and a grape on each. Place these by the sail. Add 5 sticks to either side to resemble oars.

FIND OUT ABOUT DANISH FOODS

If you would like to find out more about Danish foods, write to the Consumer Advisory Service, Danish Agricultural Producers, 2-3 Conduit Street, London W1R 0AT if you live in the United Kingdom. If you live elsewhere, write to the Danish Agricultural Marketing Board, Vester Marimagsgade 6, 1606 Copenhagen V, Denmark.

Photographs by courtesy of the Danish Food Centre.

DANWICHES WITH EYE AND APPETITE APPEAL

(see photograph above)

Back row (left to right)

Shrimps on buttered white bread with lettuce, lemon, a snippet of tomato and a touch of parsley.

Hard boiled egg and tomato slices arranged with lettuce and parsley on top of buttered brown bread.

A sardine with a lemon twist, tomato sections and lettuce with a base of buttered Danish rye bread.

Danish cheese with lettuce, black grapes, tomato, on buttered bread, brown or white.

Front row (left to right)

Cottage cheese on lettuce with a big twist of cucumber and tomato slices and cress. The base is buttered rye bread.

New potatoes boiled in their skins and sliced onto buttered rye bread with a garnish of radish and cress.

On buttered brown bread, lettuce, ham, cottage cheese and a garnish of tinned pineapple, glacé cherry and cress.

Centre

Chicken portion with lettuce and orange twist on buttered rye bread.

SUGGESTIONS FOR PICNIC DANWICHES

Liver pâté with gherkin
Mild cheese (Danbo or Samsoe) with radish
Cod's roe with tomato
Ham with cucumber
Salami with onion
Hardboiled egg slices with cress
Cheese spread with radish

PARTY TIME!

Brighten up any party with these

PATROL PURPOSE PLAN-
LITTER SURVEY

Illustrated by Linda Sandey

Why not get together with the rest of your Patrol to carry out a litter survey of your town? This is an excellent way of giving service to the community, while at the

same time learning to use your powers of imagination. Find out what you can do about your area, what you like about it and what you think could be improved on.

Different Patrols could survey different parts of the town, and you could then put all your

findings together and organise a display of the information.

First of all, decide how large an area each Patrol is going to survey. Be realistic – a small area with a number of unusual features would be more interesting than a giant plot of waste ground.

Now prepare a map of the area to be surveyed. The local library may have one which you can photocopy, or you can make your own. You can colour code the map: black – badly littered places;

red – damaged trees, etc.

Keep a checklist of the details you will need for your map. (You can use these drawings as a guide.) How many: zebra crossings, churches, telephone kiosks, pillar boxes, young trees in 'cages', parks, pubs, food shops, litter bins, bus stops, schools, playgrounds, rivers, canals? You can also make a note of specialised information which is appropriate to your area only, on the bottom of your checklist.

Your Patrol could spend an afternoon studying the way

Burton Shopping Centre,			
Man	Woman	Child	Article
			paper
			wrapper
			can
			cigarette

people behave! Make notes about who drops litter, what age they are, what they dropped. You can also enter opinions as to whether it was deliberate, through thoughtlessness, or because there was no bin nearby.

Discuss your findings and decide what to do now. Perhaps you could make posters for your school, or write to the local Council suggesting new sitings for bins? Try to think of other ideas.

If you would like to know more about this kind of activity, you will be interested in the new Pack for Youth Groups produced by the Keep Britain Tidy Group. This has lots of ideas for working with rubbish, including games and model making. Write to the Group for further details. The address is: The Keep Britain Tidy Group, Bostel House, 37 West Street, Brighton BN1 2RE.

11 a.m. – 2 p.m.

Possible reason

no bin
threw it away without thinking
to look big with friends
thoughtless
etc.

"Doesn't anyone want me?"

"a DOG is for LIFE – not just for Christmas…"

So runs the slogan on the car stickers produced by the National Canine Defence League.

It's a sad but true fact that every year in Britain thousands of puppies are bought as Christmas presents, only to be abandoned in the New Year when the family gets bored with the animal.

It is a lesser known fact, however, that many of these poor animals have been rescued and cared for by the National Canine Defence League. For almost a hundred years now, the N.C.D.L., as it is known, has existed to help dogs.

The N.C.D.L. started in the 1890s when a band of people got together to seek ways of

improving the bad conditions in which so many dogs were kept. Some of their early achievements included: securing legislation; empowering magistrates to take dogs away from cruel owners; making it an offence to chain up dogs and safeguarding dogs during Air Raids in World War Two. These and many other achievements were fought for and attained with one purpose in mind: the welfare of dogs.

Shortly after the last war the League fell on hard times and was subsequently started afresh in 1964. At this time a policy of non-destruction of dogs was adopted. This policy has continued since, except in extreme cases where it is felt that

Tiny and frightened

Just like life: rough and smooth

house some sixty dogs and they are nearly always full. It is, perhaps, a sad reflection on a country that is supposed to consider dogs as man's best friends that the N.C.D.L. have to open more centres almost annually, or as fast as funds permit.

The League is still dealing with cruelty to dogs, usually resulting from sheer ignorance on the part of the owner. They realise how important it is to educate owners and, wherever possible, give helpful advice through national and local papers, and radio. The League believe that too many people buy puppies on impulse, often as Christmas or birthday presents, but give no thought to the future well-being of these dependent animals. For this reason they have produced the car sticker which reads "A Dog Is For Life – Not Just For Christmas", over 60,000 of which have been distributed to the public.

The N.C.D.L. campaigns ceaselessly for better dog welfare. They believe that the licence fee should be raised to a sum which would cover the service of a Dog Warden at least, and that a large proportion of the Warden's role should be in educating

it would be kinder, because of severe injuries or incurable illness, to put a dog to sleep.

The main work of the National Canine Defence League is carried out at their rescue centres, of which there are now eleven around the U.K. Here the police from the districts bring the stray and abandoned dogs for rehabilitation and rehoming. On average, each kennel is able to

"I would like to get out!"

irresponsible pet-owners.

Membership of the N.C.D.L. costs only a few pounds per year. In return for this, members are automatically provided with:

a) free public liability insurance up to £100,000 on damage caused by their dog;

b) a free identity disc engraved with the owner's name and address and carrying a veterinary guarantee should the dog be injured;

c) advice on all aspects of dog ownership;

d) full voting rights in the affairs of the N.C.D.L.

The League operates three different funds to which members of the public can subscribe – but receives no state aid. All money received is given by voluntary donation. It also runs a mail order service, offering a range of gifts with an animal theme, such as calendars, candles and dog owner's diaries, just right for Christmas or birthday presents and, of course, every purchase aids League funds. If you would like to receive more details about the National Canine Defence League, contact the Secretary, N.C.D.L., 10 Seymour Street, LONDON W1H 5WB.

NATURE crossword

by Daphne Pilcher

Clues Across

1. Like a snail, but minus the shell.
3. Scottish lake.
5. Friend of Rat and Toad.
6. Plant used for basket weaving.
8. It's stripy and it stings!
9. We use it as fuel.

Clues Down

1. A marine animal with flippers.
2. Bird of the coastal cliffs.
4. The mad March one.
5. You might call it the night butterfly.
7. Young salmon.
9. A black bird, but not a blackbird!

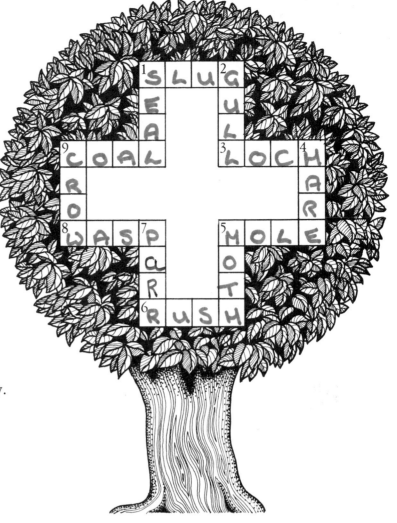

PROVERBS crossword

To complete the crossword, all you have to do is to complete the proverbs!

Clues Across:

1. Share and − − − − − alike
3. − − − − a loaf is better than none
7. Two heads are better than − − −
8. Still − − − − − − run deep
10. Too many cooks spoil the − − − − −
12. The − − − − − bird catches the worm
13. Penny wise, − − − − − foolish
15. Great oaks from little − − − − − − grow
18. Make hay while the − − − shines
19. One law for the − − − − and another for the poor
20. Cut your coat according to your − − − − −

Clues Down:

2. More − − − − − less speed
3. A − − − − − − man is an angry man
4. Pigs might − − −
5. You can't teach an old dog − − − tricks
6. − − − − − is the staff of life
9. − − − an ill wind that blows no good
10. Let not the pot call the kettle − − − − −
11. Spare the − − − and spoil the child
12. − − − − − − is as good as a feast
14. Forbidden − − − − − tastes sweetest
16. Once bitten, twice − − −
17. All is fair in love and − − −

Answers on page 61

11

IT'S A RECORD!

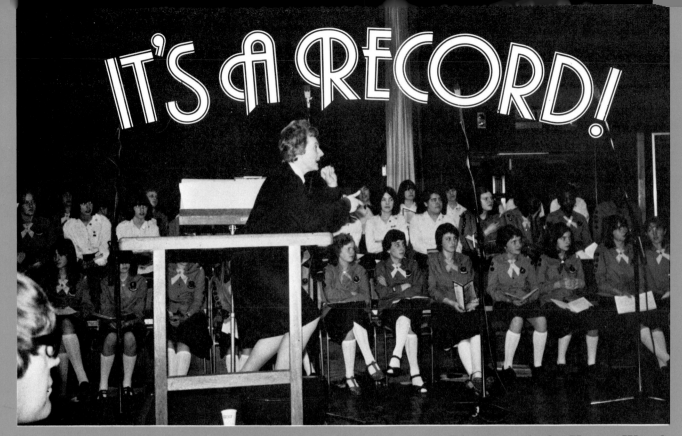

Photographs by Yvette Worth

Have you ever wondered what it would be like to sing on an LP – to be able to walk into a shop and buy a disc you have helped to make, to be able to play it and hear yourself singing?

A group of Guides and Rangers were able to find out what it was like to do all these things after they helped to make a record of many of the songs in The Girl Guide Association songbook *Songs for Tomorrow*, which was produced by the BBC.

They tell their own story...

"We weren't a trained choir. We met for the first time knowing that after seven rehearsals we would be in the recording studios recording twenty-seven songs. Everyone practised hard, learning to stand quite still; to watch the conductor all the time; to bring out every word clearly. The producer came to some of the rehearsals, listened to the songs carefully and sometimes found tiny imperfections that we hadn't noticed. We began to realise exactly how good you had to be to satisfy a producer.

"Eventually the recording weekend came and we arrived at the BBC's Maida Vale Studios.

We went down the main stairs and through a maze of passages, past doors labelled 'conductor's suite' and 'soloist'. It was almost like the centre of the earth – ceiling, walls, floor and doors were heavily soundproofed so that there was no echo. The atmosphere was quite dead. The huge 8-track machines, with their spools almost the size of dustbin

lids, would pick up nothing but the sounds that we produced, mercilessly recording every tiny mistake that would mean another 'take'. We sat on the chairs which we were going to occupy on and off for the next fifteen hours, and sang while the engineers scurried to and fro with microphones, 'balancing' us, all the while keeping in radio contact with the

engineers in the recording cubicle.

"The steel band which was to accompany four of our songs arrived. The West Indian musicians were full of jokes and let us play their 'pans'. As the notes were not in sequence we found it was difficult to play anything recognisable, but the West Indians managed to play pans, maraccas and bongoes all at the same time, with broad grins on their faces.

"We began to record. 'Here's a light', from the balancer as he pressed the red recording light button, soon became a catch-phrase. Our success was measured by the number of 'takes' it needed to make a recording which satisfied the producer. A 'take one' was very good, a 'take two' was average, and a 'take three' meant that we were slipping. We began to find out just how much concentration was needed to get a good 'take'. Comments from the producer would come over the intercom: 'That 's' was too long, someone smacked their lips, someone sniffed!' We learned that we had to be very quiet during the reverberation time – the time it takes for the sound to die away – and that one voice a fraction ahead or behind the rest of the choir or singing a wrong word meant a re-take. We learned that at the 'mixing', which is the balancing of the 8 tracks onto a final master tape, the choir can be brought 'forward', which makes the voices sound close to the microphone, or taken 'back', which makes them sound distant. We found that the balancer could also add echo but that initially the singing had to be perfectly in tune, the voices had to be absolutely 'together' and the performance had to be lively and spontaneous, as the balancer could not cover our mistakes.

"All the time we were racing against the clock. A succession of quick 'takes' and we were ahead; a problem and we fell behind the schedule. We had fifteen hours in

which to make the record; there was no coming back another time if we hadn't finished! Sometimes we had to try new sound effects, like the autoharp which sounded good at rehearsals, but terrible when recorded. Then the producer suddenly wanted a different solo voice, and auditioned a row of Guides on the spot, listening for the kind of voice that she envisaged! The chosen Guide was both horrified and excited at the chance of singing on her own on the record!

"We had a very good folk group 'backing' us and singing some of the songs. They were used to recording for the BBC and were more relaxed than we were, although one of the guitarists 'buzzed' a guitar at the wrong moment so we had to do another 'take'.

"We had our meals in the BBC canteen and looked for famous faces among the people there. We found that the dreadful things

which are said about BBC tea are quite true, but nevertheless we collected the BBC disposable cups as souvenirs!

"At last the weekend was over, and we *had* managed to record all twenty-seven songs. Our part in the making of the record was over, but we knew that many hours would be spent in mixing and editing the master tape and in listening to the test pressings again and again for the tiny sounds which we would not have noticed, but which the producer would immediately pick up. We knew that the sleeve design would be chosen and approved, and that all the business of copyright and publishing would have to be accomplished before the LP was finally launched.

"We would wait for the excitement of seeing our LP on sale in the shops, and hearing it reviewed on radio. Then we would feel really part of the huge world of sound recording!"

JUPITER JOURNAL

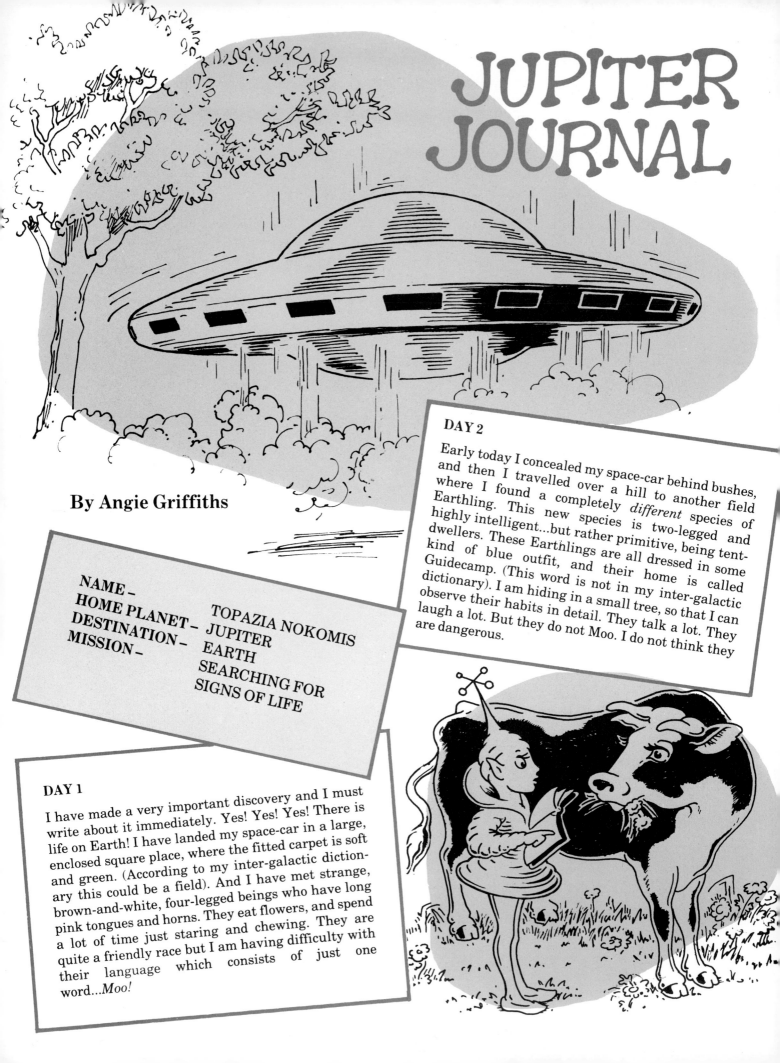

By Angie Griffiths

NAME –	TOPAZIA NOKOMIS
HOME PLANET –	JUPITER
DESTINATION –	EARTH
MISSION –	SEARCHING FOR SIGNS OF LIFE

DAY 2

Early today I concealed my space-car behind bushes, and then I travelled over a hill to another field where I found a completely *different* species of Earthling. This new species is two-legged and highly intelligent...but rather primitive, being tent-dwellers. These Earthlings are all dressed in some kind of blue outfit, and their home is called Guidecamp. (This word is not in my inter-galactic dictionary). I am hiding in a small tree, so that I can observe their habits in detail. They talk a lot. They laugh a lot. But they do not Moo. I do not think they are dangerous.

DAY 1

I have made a very important discovery and I must write about it immediately. Yes! Yes! Yes! There is life on Earth! I have landed my space-car in a large, enclosed square place, where the fitted carpet is soft and green. (According to my inter-galactic diction-ary this could be a field). And I have met strange, brown-and-white, four-legged beings who have long pink tongues and horns. They eat flowers, and spend a lot of time just staring and chewing. They are quite a friendly race but I am having difficulty with their language which consists of just one word...*Moo!*

DAY 3

Oh, I have learned much about these Earthlings. Their early-morning rituals are most interesting. First they crawl from their tents with their eyes closed – then they stagger to a bowl of cold water where they plunge in their faces and cry out. Sounds such as "Eek", "Brrr", and "Shove over, where's the soap" fill the air.

It seems that china dishes have not been invented yet. These Earthlings in their blue garments are keen on cooking – over an open fire – and they use tin a lot. Tin plates, tin mugs, tin cans and tin foil. The speed with which they can open a can of baked beans is almost faster than the speed of light.

For the first meal of the day they eat the eggs of a hen, and they drink gallons of tea. (Here is an amazing fact. The tea is diluted with something called milk, which the two-legged Earthlings collect in a jug from the four-legged Moo-beings in the next field). For the middle meal of the day they eat such things as ham and fried onions, cooked in a haybox. For the third meal they tuck into baked potatoes and sausages and omelettes. Then, when it is dark and they are zipped into bags, they eat *again*! This time they share such delicacies as tinned peaches, chocolate biscuits and crisps. I must try to get a sample of a vinegar-flavoured crisp to take home to planet Jupiter.

DAY 4

These Earthlings in the blue garments have a very complicated communication system when they are more than a field's length apart. They make secret signals by waving flags in the air. Another interesting observation is that they live in groups called Patrols, and each Patrol is called after a flower. The flower, such as a daffodil or a rose, decorates their tent and their boxes, and even the sleeves of their garments.

Earthlings have very advanced ideas on work. They use a rota, so everyone does their fair share of 'chores'. (This word not in my dictionary). I notice that they laugh a lot while 'choring', especially when dealing with soapy water and billy-cans.

This afternoon I overheard them planning a Treasurehunt. One of the older Earthlings obviously thinks she's a bird, for she calls herself Brown Owl. (She is a visitor to the camp to see her friend, "Guider". She uses a silver whistle and has a garment decorated with many badges.) Anyway, I saw this Brown Owl walking round and round the tree where I am hiding. I think she plans to conceal something in the branches for the Treasurehunt. I will have to be extra careful from now on. (What is a Treasurehunt? I must get a better dictionary!)

DAY 5

The Earthlings in blue were up at dawn to see the sunrise. Then, after breakfast, they got out maps and compasses and torches and talked about a midnight hike. This is a strange race of people – they are forever moving and talking and laughing, except for when they are sleeping (some sleep under the stars). And they have a thing about knots. Knots for this, knots for that. Sheetbend, double overhand and West Country Whip. Wait till I tell them back on Jupiter!

But danger threatens. The whistling-one called Brown Owl has been to inspect the tree again, so I must return to Jupiter. I cannot risk being captured, even though they do look a very friendly lot.

This journal will be a most valuable book for reference about these happy Earthlings. What is the secret of their happiness? Why do they *smile* so much? Some things must remain a mystery.

NAME –   TOPAZIA NOKOMIS.
DESTINATION –   HOME BASE, JUPITER.
MISSION –   TO REPORT ON HAPPY
                EARTHLINGS DRESSED
                IN BLUE.
CARGO –   ONE VINEGAR-
                FLAVOURED CRISP.
                – GRASS SAMPLE.
                – LENGTH OF STRING TO
                  SHOW CLOVE-HITCH.
                – SOUND RECORDING OF
                  MAIN-SPECIES, CHEWING
                  AND MOOING.
                – SOUND RECORDING
                  OF OTHER SPECIES,
                  CAMPFIRE SINGING.

A DESERTED WONDERLAND

Jean Brown describes camping in the Hebrides.   Photographs by Robert Lawson

Outdoor Centres nowadays are stocked with all manner of modern camping-aids and permanent sites, portaloos, entertainments and shops seem to be everywhere. Bottled gas, convenience foods and sewn-in groundsheets seem here to stay.

Not very long ago, when our Founder introduced camping to a handful of boys on Brownsea Island, it was an adventure which needed skill. Now hundreds of people, in cars, with camping gas and gaudy frame tents, holiday under canvas with little knowledge of real campcraft. Could it be that the spirit of adventure is becoming tame? Has the desire for isolation in uncluttered places gone, and with it the know-how to survive without the amenities of today?

Of course not! There are still places in the British Isles so far away from communications, entertainments and provisions that the ability to survive in all weathers, for a considerable time, is essential; places from which you cannot just go home if the weather turns against you, where you have the thrill of finding out how good your camping really is. And there are still plenty of Guides who love the challenge!

"Where are they?" eager Guides may ask. "Where, in this over-populated country of ours, can you get so far away from it all?" Well, you *can* find such places if you look deep into the countryside, climb high on a hill, wander over moorland or into a forest, or if you sail across the sea to an island. An island! That's where the magic lies for me, and for the Guides who clamour to come with me. We just cannot

resist islands, whether they be bathed in sunshine or battered by gales. Tree-less or forest-clad, low-lying or mountainous, they attract us and compel us to return.

Around our shores there are islands galore, where the tide splashes on untrodden shores, where the boat calls infrequently, where, if you can't camp well, you wish yourself at home again by the end of the first day. But you have the experience of a lifetime if you know how to keep warm and dry, full and happy so far away from security; if you love beautiful places, beaches without people, birds and flowers in plenty, fresh air, friendship and fun.

Off the north-west of Scotland are scattered the Hebridean islands, and it is to one or other of these islands that our Guides have headed year after year after year! We have boarded a crowded train, in the heart of Yorkshire, with the minimum of equipment and the maximum of enthusiasm. We have listened to the train wheels chanting, "I-love-camping-I-love islands." We have been oblivious of diesel smoke and unimpressed by the tall buildings in Glasgow. For us there has been the vision of thatched crofters' cottages and peat smoke curling into a blue sky.

We have scrambled onto the West-Highland train, still full of the clean air it has recently brought from the mountains and the glens. For hours we have sat glued to the windows as the train has wended its slow, single-track way beside forest-bordered lochs, under the shadow of rock-strewn bens and over deer-dotted moorland. Towards night we have seen the sun set golden over the sea and the islands black against its splendour. In friendship and

peace we have unrolled our sleeping bags in the comfort of the school hall of some remote fishing village and slept till morning.

The sun rises early in the north. It has already been warm on our faces as we've gone down to the pier under the pleasant burden of our rucksacks. We've heard the screeching of gulls and the Gaelic of the fishermen; we've smelled the tang of the salt sea air and known where we were going. Westwards! To the islands! To camp, in the real meaning of the word!

Along the western shores of

almost all the islands of the Hebrides lie beaches of unparalleled beauty, miles of silver sand, bleached by sunshine till it looks like snow. The machair, that green strip between the mountains and the sea, is flower studded with heartsease, bird's foot trefoil, wild orchis and wild thyme. Primroses and violets are like confetti on the banks and it is almost instinctive to throw away shoes and spend the whole fortnight blissfully and comfortably barefoot.

On the shore, beneath the machair, and cropping up at intervals behind it, is the sand, white and fine, falling from high dunes like drifting snow. Oh, the fun of leaping from the ridge, dropping . . . dropping and landing in a cloud of disturbed sand, of running with arms and legs flying, or sliding with improvised sledges down untrodden slopes!

To pitch a tent on the machair is to pitch on Nature's best carpet. Pegs grip firmly. No sewn-in

groundsheets for us! It would be sacrilege to cover and fade such a carpet!

No bottled gas either for Guides who live like sandpipers on the shore. If the island has forests there will be pine strippings in plenty. If tree-less, there is driftwood hurled ashore by winter gales. The crofters will provide peat. It burns better than coal, produces a heat comparable to a furnace and ensures hot food quickly and deliciously prepared. And, if the season is dry, there are scanjechs, the thoroughly dried-out droppings of the cattle which have strayed onto the beach or wintered on the machair.

To live on the shore is to leave behind the amenities which have inevitably crept into camps on County and permanent sites. Lats will be dug deeply and frequently, for the chore of digging is the ageless game of discovering Australia. Elsans! Whoever heard of them?

On the shore we become resourceful and acquisitive. From the high-watermark come bottles, bowls and herring boxes to supplement the few utensils we have brought. Scraps of old fishing nets and sun-bleached crates become valuable pieces of furniture. Driftwood, selectively gathered, is woven into our gadgets.

Blessed sand! It makes a bed unequalled by any Lilo, it supports grass so hardy that no amount of wear and tear or rain disturbs the colour or the pile, and it accepts water so greedily that spills are of no consequence.

Wash tents are unnecessary and, when wind blows away plates and rain re-wets them, washing up can be done in the D'abri.

In the 'banking', behind the fireplace, the large oven can be buried so that our menu can daily include fruit tarts and crumbles, meat and potato and shepherd's pies! We sample limpets and carragheen (seaweed), gratefully receive a bucketful of newly-caught fish, eat crowdie (the local cream cheese) with everything. Often we gather baskets of mushrooms and occasionally we enjoy lobster. In one of the crofter's houses we make a cloutie dumpling, and generally eat and eat and eat!

Resourceful and acquisitive we must be. Inventive we become. Countless games are played on the shore with shells and rocks, flotsam and jetsam brought in with the tide and oddments from our camp equipment. The shore becomes our sports field for races and competitions – some of them aquatic, all of them hilarious. Our annual Fancy Dress Parade lacks nothing because our wardrobe is so limited. Seaweed will make any Guide into Neptune, and with straw and a blanket a scarecrow you can be. Treasure and scavenger hunts, creative play with fragile shells and strong glue or plaster appeal every year.

"Freedom is being in camp in the Hebrides", wrote Julie. "We go to camp on an island so that we can do as we like," wrote Rachel.

It seems that way! If we feel like climbing and there is no cloud on the mountains then, suitably shod and clad, we tackle Ben Luskentyre. If we feel like rising early and walking we find that Hebridean roads joyously follow the coastline. The North Atlantic can crash upon rocks, a seething mass of broken water, Arctic green and truly magnificent, but it can also mirror the vivid blue of the sky and lap so gently on the beach one thinks oneself in paradise.

Islands are small. A stout heart and sturdy legs can encircle an island in a day. By shore and water-lillied lochan the roads wind between scattered crofts and peaceful harbours. We chat frequently with crofters cutting peat or tending potatoes. We lean over the fank and watch them shearing and we pause to discover how they mend their fishing nets and lobster creels and how they dye their fleeces in a cauldron by a stream.

If it is haymaking time we see them cutting small plots with the clean sweeps of a scythe, and hanging the drying hay on a fence to hurry its crispening before rain falls. If it is wet we crowd into their weaving sheds and watch their spinning wheels and see the tweed grow before the flying shuttle of their hand-operated looms.

The weather can be very hot and then we are lazy, and brown ourselves like natives by spending long hours in the sunshine, swimming frequently and drinking gallons of squash. But it can be cold and wet and then we gather in the D'abri for charades and stunts and yarns. Our guitarist strums away and we sing prematurely and do not wait for the evening campfire which ends each day. There is great joy in singing together until the darkness falls and the corncrake ceases its croaking in the corn.

We sing every night, unless we dance! If Calum will lend his barn and air his pipes and Neil will bring out his accordion we will dance until morning and not feel weary.

Freedom to do as we like sounds selfish and unworkable, but we who go camping in the Hebrides are friends and "Friendship is a thing of harmony". The crofters, too, are our friends. They are the most hospitable people in the British Isles. They speak a different language, live a different life and inhabit the fringe of the Atlantic, but their warmth and humour are unequalled.

Learn to camp well, all you who love beautiful places, and be able to leave the cluttered world behind and head for remote places where you can really put your Guiding skills, and yourself, to the test.

Fashion is FUN!

by Jil Shipley

So long as you obey a few basic rules!

THIN LEGS?

DON'T WEAR:

Very short skirts which show your bony knees! High heeled shoes, which make your legs look longer, and therefore thinner still.

DO WEAR:

Longish full skirts and trousers in all styles, fitting or baggy. In the winter months you'll look good in leg warmers, and all year round you can wear short socks and flat shoes. Shoes should not be heavy or 'clumpy', but ankle straps look good on you, and you can wear all sorts of coloured and patterned tights.

FAT LEGS?

DON'T WEAR:

Too short or too tight skirts; tight trousers; ankle-strapped shoes or ankle socks, or shoes which are very strappy and delicate.

DO WEAR:

Longish skirts with toning tights and medium-heeled shoes; boots, Oxford bag trousers which give a good overall line; pretty eye-catching blouses and jumpers, which draw attention away from your legs. And a smile – that will work too!

DON'T WEAR:

Clothes of any kind which fit closely around the waist, which will only emphasise the problem. Belts, which will draw attention exactly to the area you would rather hide! Blouses and tops tucked into your skirts and trousers.

DO WEAR:

Dresses which flare gently, without a 'waisted' shape. Loose tunics, smocks, and other tops which are just long enough to cover the 'problem area'. Choose co-ordinating separates which don't break up the overall line, and always go for flared styles in general, rather than gathered.

DON'T WEAR:

Trousers with tops tucked in, which may look fine from the front, but not so good from behind! The same goes for skirts, and for dresses with a fitted line, in which the bottom has no alternative but to stick out! Skirts very gathered at the waist, with extra bulk around the hips.

DO WEAR:

Trousers with loose tops, as in the 'big tummy' picture, will have the same camouflaging effect for a big bottom. Skirts which are only slightly gathered, to give concealing fullness. Flared dresses, as in the 'too fat' picture, which will drape easily over the bottom, and give the good overall line which is always fashion's greatest single consideration.

BIG TUMMY?

BIG BOTTOM?

DON'T WEAR:

Very short or very severely tied-back hairstyles, which create a 'pin-head' effect. Very close-fitting clothes, which emphasise your slimness, but also make you look inches taller!

DO WEAR:

A soft, and if possible voluminous hairstyle, with pretty combs and slides, which will help to balance your height. Baggy trousers and wide-shouldered shirts and jackets. Full skirts in a length just around the knee. Sturdy, flattish shoes, or medium heeled for smarter occasions.

DON'T WEAR:

A big or fussy hairdo, which will make your head look too big for your body. Large slides or combs in your hair. Fussy clothes in 'pretty-pretty' patterns, which will make you look like a small child all dressed up for a birthday party! Too much jewellery or wide belts.

DO WEAR:

Your hair tied back, or in a pony tail. If you have long hair, pull the fronts up and back and secure them with slides or side combs. Fringes often suit short girls. Keep clothes simple, and go for toning colours which give a co-ordinated overall look. Medium heeled shoes, or slightly higher if you can walk comfortably in them.

TOO TALL?

TOO SHORT?

22

TOO THIN?

TOO FAT?

DON'T WEAR:

Straight, fitted clothes which emphasise your shape – or lack of it! Belts, which draw you in even further. Severely tied-back hairstyles. High-heeled strappy shoes, which complete the impression of daintiness, not to say, scrawniness!

DO WEAR:

You're lucky, you can wear all sorts of big, dramatic shapes, loose-fitting, baggy, gathered, and so on, which most other girls are always longing to wear, but can't. A full hairstyle will complete the picture, and you'll also look good in lots of layers, which is a favourite fashion idea.

DON'T WEAR:

Drainpipe trousers, which were meant for people with drainpipe shapes. Tight-fitting T-shirts or other clothes which reveal bulges around your midriff. Flat shoes, unless you're very tall, or don't feel comfortable in heels.

DO WEAR:

Flared dresses which give a good overall line. Carefully co-ordinated skirts and tops, which do the same. Shoes with a medium heel to make you look slightly taller and therefore slimmer. A soft hairstyle to frame your face, but nothing too fussy. Toning tights and shoes.

THE SURVIVORS

Longhorn Cow and Calf

Of all domestic breeds of cattle today, the Warwickshire Longhorn is probably the nearest direct descendant of the wild cattle (Bos primigenius), domesticated by Stone Age Man. The Neolithic cave paintings of cattle with wide-spanned horns are very similar to the Longhorns at Cotswold Farm Park. Although attractive animals, they are not popular as farm cattle today, and in fact there are only about 250 cows left in Britain.

Jacob Ram

These attractive 'spotted' sheep, of which only around 3,000 exist in Britain, have a fascinating history. In the book of Genesis it is written that while Jacob was working as a shepherd, he was told that he would be allowed to keep all the spotted sheep born in the flock as payment for his work. The bible tells how Jacob, by the use of magic spotted wands, increased the number of spotted sheep considerably! It was probably from their wool that he made the Coat of Many Colours for his favourite son, Joseph.

Look at the photographs on this page. Do the animals seem at all unusual to you? Or would you say that they are the type of livestock which can be found on any ordinary farm nowadays?

In fact, these animals are very rare indeed, and are only in existence today thanks to the efforts of concerned people, such as the staff of the Rare Breeds Survival Centre near Cheltenham. Cotswold Farm Park specialises in breeding domestic animals which would otherwise almost certainly become extinct. The Farm opens its doors to the public every Summer, and with its many different animals, pets' corner and information centre, has a variety of items guaranteed to suit all ages. If you are interested in finding out more about rare breeds of domestic animals write to the address at the foot of the page for further details.

Buff Turkeys

All the Turkeys at Cotswold Farm Park are descended from the American wild bush turkey. The Buff Turkey was developed by the Victorians, who also bred buff ducks and chickens. It is a good egg layer, but cannot compete with the broader, white breed common today, so is almost extinct.

Cotswold Farm Park is open from March to September and is situated near the A40 Oxford-Cheltenham Road. Send a large S.A.E. for further information, opening times, etc. to: Cotswold Farm Park, Guiting Power, Cheltenham, Gloucestershire.

ALL LEFT-ALL RIGHT?

by Fiona Lawson Illustrated by Royston Edwards

Cackhander, corrie fister, southpaw, kitty wessy . . . whatever you call them, one in eleven people today is left handed. That's a lot of people!

So just why is left-handedness thought of as being a little bit odd? The idea probably originates from the fact that the Latin word for left was 'sinister'. When 'sinister' acquired the extra meaning of 'nasty', all sorts of rumours started up – and have been going around ever since.

In fact, things seem to have been going against left-handers as far back as Biblical times. For every single mention of left-handedness in the Bible (all of them bad, incidentally) there are four mentions of the right hand (all good!).

In Europe, there has long been a superstition that it is unlucky to meet a left-handed person on a Tuesday morning. The origins of

this story can be traced back to Tiw, the Scandinavian God of War, who was left-handed. He gave his name to a day of the week – Tiw's day – our modern Tuesday. Hence the superstition.

Worse still, in the Middle Ages, left-handed men were thought to be devils in disguise and were tortured for their sins until they 'confessed', whereupon they were put to death. The fair sex didn't come off any better – left-handed women were believed to be witches and were drowned as punishment. If by any chance they survived the ducking stool and came up still alive, this was taken as confirmation that they really were witches, and they were then burned at the stake!

Gamblers have always maintained that it is unlucky to pick up the cards with the left hand – although this particular superstition is probably based on

commonsense, as it is very difficult for left handers *or* right handers to fan out the cards and look at the numbers when holding them in the left hand. Just try it!

With all these unfavourable points weighted against being left-handed, you might well be surprised that there are any left-handed people around in the world today! Or at least, that they actually admit to being left-handed! Fortunately, however, doctors have gradually come to understand what causes left-handedness, and now realise that there is nothing 'sinister' about it.

In fact, the real explanation seems to be that the human brain, which is actually split into two halves, uses one side to control each side of the body. Each half of the brain controls the *opposite* side of the body. Most people are ruled by the left-hand side of the brain but every so often someone is born with a predominant right-hand side. Just why this is, no-one yet knows.

Until quite recently, school teachers actively discouraged left-handedness in pupils, believing it to be an unnatural state. A favourite 'cure' was to tie the left hand of the unfortunate pupil behind his back, while

another trick was to seat the left-hander at a double desk (on the right hand side) so that the arm of the person sitting next to the 'leftie' would dig into him as he was writing and force him, for comfort's sake, to use his right hand. It is undoubtedly true that forcing a child to be right-handed when he doesn't want to be can cause a lot of mental distress. It is frequently said that this practice can make a child stammer, and although there is no sound proof of this, it is certainly true that the Queen's father, King George VI, grew up with a very bad stammer. He was a left-hander who resisted attempts to make him right-handed when he was young.

The number of left-handed people in this country seems to be growing all the time. Ten years ago it was reckoned that one in every seventeen persons was left-handed – now it is nearer one in eleven. The reason for this is simply that more children are being encouraged to follow their natural tendencies.

Nevertheless, it is undoubtedly still a right-handed world. Look around you – everything, it seems, is geared to the right

hand. Think of left-handed people peeling potatoes (backwards) or lifting a soup spoon (and having to transfer it to the other hand). Think of door handles, and staircase handrails. Think of irons, with the flex inconveniently coming out in front of left-handers so that they continually have to push it away as they work. Think of address books, with the flick tabs on the right-hand side. The list of difficulties is endless. Playing most musical instruments is difficult for lefties, too, as they have to learn 'backwards'. Learning to knit and crochet usually cause the same problems.

Writing causes 'lefties' endless problems. Even in these enlightened days, left-handed children are still usually the last in their class to learn to write. At least nowadays there are ballpoint pens which hardly smudge at all – spare a thought for all the left-handers growing up in the days of fountain pens, smudging the still wet ink on the paper as their left hand rested on top of what they had just written.

The British way of writing, of course, is just not designed for left-handers. It slopes across the page from left to right and can really only be done satisfactorily by pulling the pen across the page behind you. You may well notice, if you look at your left-handed friends, that the girls have a different way of writing than the boys. This is because the automatic way for a left-hander to use a pen or pencil is to *push* it across the page (while right-handers pull it). To do this, your fingers must be quite strong and you must have full control of

them. Girls generally develop finger control very early on in life and, if left alone and not influenced by right-handers, will teach themselves to write in this way. Boys, on the other hand, don't develop strong finger control until later in life, and therefore have to write by hooking the wrist right round the pen ('crab fisted') and pulling it across the page. This looks very odd to a right-hander, and in fact is very uncomfortable if writing for any length of time, but it *is* one way round the problem!

Help is at hand (pardon the pun) however, for left-handers who despair of ever being able to do anything 'properly'. Various enlightened manufacturers now produce left-handed items, such as irons and kitchen knives. Often these goods are not prominently displayed, so it's always as well to ask if shops stock left-handed versions when buying these items. There is also a super shop in London called 'Anything Left-Handed Ltd.' which stocks a large range of everyday items specially designed for left-handed people. There are left-handed pens, playing cards, potato peelers, irons, knives, tin openers – not to mention a range of badges, books and posters proclaiming their message to the world in the form of witty slogans like 'You've A Right To Be Left!'

The shop runs a mail order service and will send you a list of all their goods, with current prices, if you send them a large addressed envelope along with two loose first class stamps. Their address is Anything Left Handed Ltd., 65 Beak Street, London W1R 3LF.

So you see, it isn't so bad being left-handed after all. All Guides and Brownies, of course, use the special left handshake – and if you *are* left-handed, you're certainly in good company. Napoleon, Caesar, Leonardo da Vinci, John McEnroe, Martina Navratilova and Paul McCartney all share the distinction – so don't feel left out!

It's all YOURS!

Last year we ran a competition in *Today's Guide* magazine, asking for Guides to send their poems or stories for this year's annual. Here are the prizewinning entries.

GUIDING

Seventy-one years have passed since Guiding was begun,
Tell me what has made it last for you and everyone,
What made it last through peacetime, through troubles and through war,
How has it reached its numbers of six million or more?

It's changed throughout its history to keep up with the times
The Challenges have altered, but no one seems to mind.
The uniform has changed too, no hats with brims so wide,
But Guiding's still the fun it was when granny was a Guide.

Guides still try to do their best, helping others who're in need,
A Brownie Guide does a good turn, a Guide does a good deed,
Companies still go camping, in summer and in spring,
Exploring, tracking, First Aid, and lots of other things.

It's my belief that Guiding will last for years to come
And Guides the whole world over think of Olave as their Mum.
She'll be regarded highly and so will dear B.-P.
By Scouts and Guides and Brownies and others such as we.

**First Prize Winner –
Sarah Faulks
of Ewell,
Surrey
Aged: 15.**

Second Prize Winner –
Sandra Hart
of Brightlingsea,
Essex.
Age: 14.

GUIDES GO TO SEA

It was a lovely morning, the sun was out, and only a few clouds were scattered overhead. Cissie could hear the gentle water rippling against the side of the boat. Except for this there seemed to be a total silence.

It was only the day before that Cissie's patrol had gone out to a friend's boat. The boat was called *The Mersey Pirate* and was quite a large boat, with a big cabin, from which ran a short flight of steps leading to the sleeping quarters. As these were quite small, Joanne and Susie had brought camp beds to sleep on, while Janet and Cissie, the older two, had the single beds provided. The two rooms were nicely furnished with one cupboard, two chests of drawers and a large, comfortable chair.

Cissie looked older for her age than she really was, at fourteen. She was quite pretty with her clear blue eyes and her blonde hair which she wore curled at the ends. Cissie was a constant Guide – she had an armful of badges and was well on her way to becoming a Queen's Guide.

Cissie went below and woke everybody up. Soon everyone was dressed in jeans and old pullovers, except Joanne the youngest, who wore a dark olive dress with white cuffs and a green ribbon in her hair. She had a smile on her face as she clambered up the stairs – she was a bright girl but wasn't very interested in Guides but always did her best.

"What are we going to do this morning?" asked Susie as she appeared at the top of the stairs with Janet, Cissie's Patrol Second.

"I'm not sure yet, but I suppose we could have a picnic on that island," pointed out Cissie.

"Yes, let's!"

So after breakfast, which was eaten in haste, the children packed a lunch big enough for a whole army and then clambered down into a little dinghy they had found on board.

When the children reached the shore they dragged the dinghy up the beach so that it didn't float away.

The children then walked along the beach for what seemed like hours; they then finally decided to sit down on the beach and have lunch. Afterwards they sat around lazily, until the clouds got darker and the sun went in, and a cold wind began to blow up with a drizzle of rain.

They quickly packed up all their things and put them in their bags, and all of them began to run

27

together for somewhere to keep them dry.

"Look, some caves," pointed out Janet.

The children ran towards the caves just in time before the rain poured down.

"Made it," squealed Susie, out of breath.

"Can we see where these caves lead to?" asked Joanne.

"Why not? Come on!" replied Cissie.

So they walked into the gloomy darkness at the back of the caves. It was cold in there, so the children pulled on their cardigans to keep warm, and stayed close together. They were now getting further and further into the cave.

"What's that noise?" quivered Joanne.

The noise sounded like a fast shuffling. It was getting closer, and louder, and now there was a huge shadow on the opposite side of the cave! It ran straight in front of them.

"It's a boy!" giggled Janet.

"Let's run after him and ask him the way out of this stupid cave," suggested Cissie, feeling a little lost.

So they followed him. The boy seemed to be getting faster and faster, and soon the children had lost him and were even more lost than ever themselves.

They were getting very tired now, as they had been on their feet most of the afternoon.

"What's the time?" asked Cissie.

"Six o'clock," answered Janet. "Time's flown."

"Have we got anything left to eat?" asked Joanne.

"Yes," answered Cissie, looking through the bag. So the children sat on a ledge at the side of the cave and ate what was left of their lunch. It wasn't much, but they didn't complain.

The younger two of the four, Joanne and Susie, were getting very tired and when they all set off again they very soon began to lag behind. Joanne began to walk clumsily.

"Aaaah!" she screamed, as she fell down with a bang.

"Are you all right?" asked Cissie.

"Hey, look what she fell over!" said Janet, before Joanne could answer.

"It's a box!" exclaimed Susie, thankful for a chance for a little rest, but too shy to ask for one before.

Joanne was now sitting on the dusty floor of the cave feeling a bit shaken, and Janet had taken her penknife out of her pocket and was desperately trying to open the box.

"It won't budge," said Janet in vain.

"Let me have a go," said Cissie, taking the box out of Janet's hands.

"Look what's inside!" yelled Janet as Cissie managed to prize the box open. Janet grabbed a handful of watches!

"Put them back!" commanded Cissie.

"I wonder where they came from?" said a puzzled Susie.

"Maybe the boy dropped them," suggested Janet.

"Good thinking," cried Cissie. "Let's go!"

So the children got up and followed the footsteps, which they had cleverly found in the dust. The

BEING A GOLDFISH MUST BE NICE

Must be nice being a goldfish
In a pond or in a tank
You wouldn't go shopping
Or have money in the bank.

Must be nice being a goldfish
Blowing bubbles all day long
You wouldn't have school dinners
Or be scolded for doing wrong.

Must be nice being a goldfish
Not a pussy or a pup
You wouldn't have to go to school
Or do the washing up.

Must be horrid being a goldfish
People staring through to see
You swimming there in boredom
I think I'll stay as me.

**Third Prize Winner –
Katherine Owen
of Crewe,
Cheshire.
Age: 11.**

If you would like to try your hand at a prize competition, turn to page 60 now!

footsteps seemed to come to an end at one point, until they found a hole in the cave wall wide enough to climb through. Cissie scrambled over to the hole – it was about 40 centimetres high and about 60 centimetres wide. They crawled slowly through the gap and then jumped down about a metre to the rock floor of another cave below, which they could only just see now as the light was fading. The cave stretched out a long way before them, and in the distance they could just make out three tunnels forking off in different directions.

"Look, the boy!" shouted Janet.

"Follow him!" ordered Cissie.

The children charged after him at full pelt. The boy, noticing this, ran even faster.

They were beginning to slow down now as they had been moving for a good hour. The boy didn't realise it, but he had run down a dead end tunnel.

"Oh, no," he shouted when he was faced with a dead end wall with nowhere to turn. The girls surrounded him.

"All right, I give in, I'll come quietly," said the boy, who looked about the same age as the elder girls.

"What does he mean?" whispered Janet to Cissie.

"I've seen his face before somewhere," whispered Cissie back. "Yes, I know, aren't you the boy with your picture in the paper for stealing watches from the jeweller's. They've been after you..."

The boy didn't listen to any more but suddenly made a dash for it, knocking Joanne flat, but he ran into trouble when he came against Cissie, who was as strong as any boy. Cissie grabbed his arm and pulled it behind his back. She then borrowed Joanne's ribbon and tied a knot in it very tight so that not even she could get it undone, and tied his wrists together with it.

Joanne wasn't badly hurt, except for a few cuts on her knee.

Cissie forced the boy, with the help of the other three, to lead them out of the cave.

It wasn't long before all five were on board *The Mersey Pirate*.

The girls then travelled to the mainland to take their prisoner to the police, who were overwhelmed to see the boy captured at last. The children went back to the boat to have a good rest, as it was now evening.

The next morning they were just getting up when a small boat came alongside them and a policeman got out and came aboard.

"Good morning, girls," he called.

"Hello," responded the Guides.

"I've come to give you a reward from the shop owner for those watches you found," he said and handed Cissie an envelope.

"Oh, thank you!" replied the girls.

Inside was ten pounds, as they soon discovered.

"How lovely!" exclaimed Janet.

"When you four grow up, give me a ring and I might sign you on as police detectives," joked the policeman.

All the children burst out laughing as they followed the policeman off the boat to have a well earned breakfast on the mainland.

TURN OVER A NEW LEAF!

Why not resolve to try a new crafts idea this year? All you need to do is collect a handful of leaves from a park or garden and you have the basic 'ingredients' of these two pretty aprons. The designs are very simple to copy and won't cost much to make: you need a plain apron or two, your collection of leaves, and some Dylon products.

Both of the aprons were made from plain white fabric: on the left, a 'positive' leaf design has been printed on with fabric paint, and on the right, leaves were used as a template for a 'negative' wax and dye batik apron. Here's how to make your own aprons:

Leaf printing: the positive pattern

Wash and iron your fabric. Cotton or linen are best, but any cotton mixture, such as polyester/cotton will do just as well. If you are lucky, you will already have a plain white apron all ready to use. If not, buy a piece of material of a suitable size. Perhaps you might like to make a waist apron rather than one which has a bodice, like the aprons shown here. In any case, you will find that a piece of plain white material won't be too expensive – look out for remnants in the sales. If you don't have a ready-made apron, draw the outline of the apron shape on your material in pencil, so that you don't end up making a pattern off the edge of the garment!

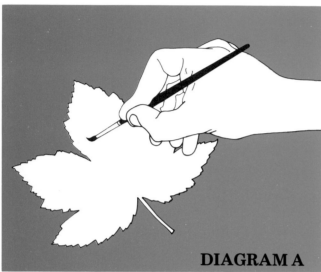

DIAGRAM A

Now arrange the leaves into an attractive pattern on your apron. Take your time over this and experiment until you have an arrangement which you really like. Now, picking up each leaf in turn, paint one side (see diagram 'A'), with Dylon Color-fun fabric paint. (We used 'Cosmic Blue', but there are lots of other shades to choose from.) There are full instructions for use on the pack. Now place the leaf paint side downwards onto the material and press it firmly, then remove the leaf and you will find it has formed a delicate 'positive' imprint. When the paint is completely dry, cover the area with a clean cotton cloth, a teatowel will do – and press with a hot iron to fix the paint, so that the design is permanent.

Leaf batik:
the negative pattern

First, wash and iron your apron or piece of fabric. Again, cotton or linen are best. Now pin the material taut on an old picture frame or across the top of a wooden box or drawer. (Diagram B). Be extra careful to make sure that the material really is stretched tight, as sagging cloth will stop the design working effectively. Arrange the leaves in an attractive pattern on the material. Now melt some candle wax or batik wax (available from craft shops) in a heatproof dish. Be very careful with the hot wax

– it is safest to do this with the dish of wax standing in a pan of water. When the wax is hot enough – it should appear transparent when applied to the fabric – paint over each leaf using a thick paintbrush, radiating the strokes outwards round the edge of each leaf. When the area all round the leaf has been covered, remove the leaf.

Now mix up a tin of Dylon Cold Dye with salt and a sachet of Dylon Cold Fix. (Full instructions for use come with the tin of dye.) Mix them together in a plastic bucket and then dunk the fabric into it for the required length of time (see instructions). We used Ultra Violet, but you can choose from a whole range of shades. If you are using a dark colour, it is as well to wear rubber gloves, and always be careful that the liquid does not splash out of the bucket.

When removed from the dye, the outline of each leaf will show up as a white 'negative' design on a dark background. Let the fabric dry. To remove the wax, press the fabric with a hot iron through two or three layers of newspaper, then wash in hot soapy water.

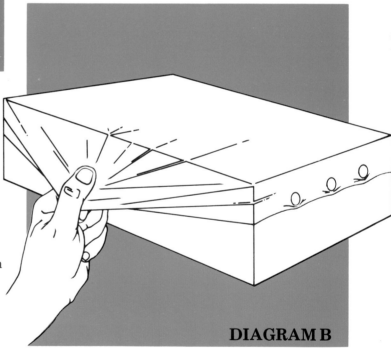

DIAGRAM B

These aprons make super Christmas or birthday presents, but you'll probably want to make one for yourself first! Once you've mastered the technique – it's very easy really – you can experiment with all sorts and sizes of leaves. A border of small beech leaves, for example, would look very pretty round the hem of an apron, with perhaps a matching trim round the pockets.

Of course there's no need to work with aprons all the time. Leaf patterns look just as effective on tablecloths, skirts, scarves . . . we'll *leaf* the choice up to you!

Bristol Evening Post

UP TO RANGERS

WHAT ARE RANGERS – DO YOU KNOW?

by Brenda Hughes

Are there any Rangers near you, perhaps meeting where you hold your Company meeting? Do Rangers take part in or help with District events, or do they appear only on special occasions when they look smart and attractive in their crisp, aquamarine blouses and neat forage-type hats?

Rangers are girls of 14 to 18 who have either been Guides and want to continue Guiding with their friends, or girls who have never experienced Guiding but are attracted by the activities of a particular Ranger unit.

What are those activities? What sort of things do Rangers do? To find out, let's listen in to a Ranger Executive Meeting. (That's the equivalent of the Patrol Leaders' Council.)

After their investiture the 128th St Oswald's Ranger Unit have a ride on a High Speed Train.

Sally – *(Chairman of the Executive Committee, one of the Rangers)* Right, let's get started, we've got a lot of decisions to make tonight and I don't want to be late home, because I have some homework to do. Can we have the Minutes of the last meeting, please, Linda?

The Secretary reads the Minutes.

Sally – Has anyone any corrections to make? *(Pause)* Right, then I'll sign them. Now, the first item on the agenda is our programme up to Christmas. What suggestions have we had?

Mandy – I've been asked to suggest at least one all-night walk, preferably on a Saturday night.

Suzanne – Some of the younger ones want to do some handicrafts – the sort that are really useful, such as basketry, lace-making, and good Christmas decorations.

Mandy – Yes, things made out of those sheets of plastic foil you can get at craft shops, so that they'll last. They're also interested in whittling and wood carving.

Tracy – I've been asked to suggest a cycling weekend with the Venture Scouts, using Youth Hostels – and can we do some real orienteering?

The Forty Hill Rangers enjoy a sponsored disco dance in aid of Enfield's talking newspaper for the blind. They raised £300.

North London Weekly Advertiser

Two Rangers try their hand at basket weaving during a craft workshop at Gawthorpe School, Padiham.

Burnley Evening Star

Joanne – Jill would like us to cover some of the *Design for Living* clause of the Duke of Edinburgh Award Scheme. That's really all she has to do to complete her Silver.

Sarah – I would like a course on heraldry, because I want to do that for my Ranger Challenge. Also, it ties in with brass rubbing, which four people have asked for. Some of the Venture Scouts are interested in it too.

Sally – Skip, have you got anything you want to add to the list?

Skip – *(the Ranger Guider)* – Well, if we are going on this walking holiday in Switzerland with the Venture Scouts next summer we need to do some training and have someone in to tell us about clothing and equipment and lightweight camping. We shouldn't leave it until the last minute. Also, we should be thinking about raising funds for that holiday.

Sally – Yes, and there's the Christmas Service Project. We must get that sorted out so that we can get on with it. Any other suggestions before we try to make out a programme?

Mandy – Yes, what are we doing about a Christmas dinner this year? It was so expensive last year, going out to that restaurant. Couldn't we cook our own and have it here? We could put up decorations and bring some nice crockery and cutlery and have a good evening much more cheaply.

Joanne – I think that's a marvellous idea.

Sarah – We could have it on a Saturday evening so that we could spend the afternoon preparing for it.

Tracy – How about inviting the Venture Scouts?

Mandy – That's a good idea. We could have candles and background music and really make it as good as any restaurant.

Sally – Right. Now Linda, will you read out the list of ideas suggested so far, please?

Linda – Here goes:
1. All-night walk, preferably on a Saturday.
2. Basketry.
3. Lace-making.
4. Good Christmas decorations which will last a few years.
5. Whittling and wood carving.
6. Cycling weekend.
7. Orienteering.
8. *Design for Living* clause of D. of E.
9. Heraldry and brass rubbing with the Venture Scouts.
10. Preparation for holiday.
11. Christmas Service Project.
12. Christmas dinner.

That's the lot!

Tracy – Quite enough too, if we've got to get all that in before Christmas.

Sally – I've drawn up this chart of the weeks and weekends between now and Christmas, so let's see how much we can get in.

A fairly wide-ranging programme, isn't it? There are a lot more ideas in the Ranger Handbook. If you're wondering about joining Rangers, why not get hold of a Handbook and have a good look at it. Then, if possible, talk to some Rangers and find out what *they* do, as each Unit varies.

Having been a Ranger myself and a Ranger Guider I know how much fun it can be and how much adventure is waiting round the corner, so why not come and join us?

A SIGN of the TIMES

by Jean Homewood

This shield belongs to a married couple, both entitled to use a coat-of-arms

This man's mother inherited her arms (top right-hand quarter) and so he can use them as well as those of his father

Next time you take off your Guide tie, have a good look at your County badge. Do you know why it bears that design? Have you ever stopped to wonder why we wear badges? Why not just a label like our Company nametape?

Next time you take off your school blazer, have a good look at your school badge. If a new girl asked you about it, could you explain the design to her?

Next time you pass a public house, look at the sign board. I expect there's a picture of the name – but why not just words?

Finding out the answers to these and other questions would certainly be 'thinking for yourself' and could lead you to a fascinating and absorbing hobby. Spotting different pub signs, by the way, is a very popular hobby and one that can help to pass the time on long car journeys. If you don't travel very often, just concentrate on the ones near to where you live – it's amazing how many you'll find once you start looking for them! All you need is a note-book and a pair of observant eyes, so no one could complain that it is an expensive pastime. If you decide to 'collect' pub signs for your Collector Badge, however, I think you must be prepared to draw them to show to your tester, or to take photographs, which would be quicker but definitely more expensive.

Even if you don't have your Collector badge in mind, do take the trouble to be systematic, and then you will get more pleasure out of your records later on. Columns headed 'Name' (of the pub), 'Place', 'Date', and an extra one for anything special you want to remember, will make life easier if you are in a moving car and the driver can't be persuaded to stop. Every second page could be left blank for little sketches.

Once you start looking round properly, sooner or later you will find a pub named 'The *something-or-other* Arms'. You have probably seen the Royal Coat-of-Arms, or may have a school badge of this kind. They crop up in various places such as banks and town halls. Sports clubs and universities have them, and at least half the T-shirts worn nowadays have a badge of some sort!

All these badges are much more decorative than plain writing, but how did they come about in the first place?

Back we go a few hundred years . . . to the days when Kings

Baden-Powell

The Royal Arms as used today

Illustrated by Kate Lloyd-Jones

33

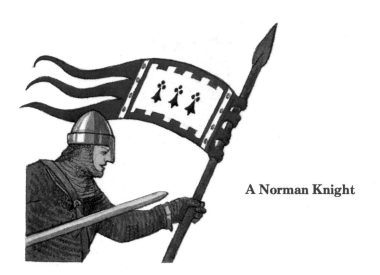

A Norman Knight

A Crusader

led their own troops into battle. The King and the chief nobles each had their own personal standard (flag) which was always carried with them. Many of the emblems on these flags were later transferred to the part of the country from which their owners came and are still in use today by cities and county councils. Kent, for instance, still uses the white horse brought over by the early Saxon invaders; I wonder what they would have chosen if Hengist and Horsa had stayed at home? This was sufficient until about the time of the Norman invasion, when something more complicated was needed. We can see by looking at pictures of the Bayeux Tapestry that it must have been extremely difficult to tell Norman from Saxon, as everyone wore the same kind of chain mail.

Another hundred years . . . and tournaments, or mock battles,

A shield for a man, a lozenge (diamond) for a woman

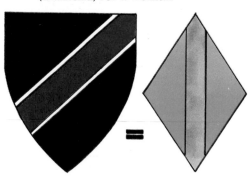

had become as popular as football matches are today, with valuable prizes for the victors, and the onlookers taking sides and laying bets that their favourite knights would win. Now, a man in full armour is completely unrecognisable, so some form of identification became essential. As very few people could read in those days it would have been useless to have 'William de Clare' written on one's front and back, so each knight adopted a 'device' (pattern or symbol) that only he could use. Sometimes these devices advertised how brave he was – a lion or a bear or a wild boar – or they could be a 'pun' on his name. The Queen Mother's family name is Bowes-Lyon, and her standard shows this in pictorial form. Since the whole point of this system was that only one man should use a particular device, the king's heralds kept records and settled any arguments. The device would be displayed on a knight's shield and on the coat he wore over his armour, which was called a coat-of-arms. Gradually the term came to be used for the device rather than the garment and, since the heralds were in charge of it all, everything to do with them has become known as 'heraldry'.

Coats-of-arms were used on clothing and servants' liveries (uniforms), and almost always on their owner's tomb or monument.

If your parish church is over two hundred years old you may see one there. Like the one displayed on the pub sign, (The . . . Arms), it will belong to a family which was prominent in your neighbourhood in the past; or, of course, they may still be. Even if the family has moved away or the family line died out, their arms may still be used by your town or borough council; if they were patrons or founders of local schools then part of their arms is probably used in the school badge; have you made a note to find out about your badges? The arms of Eton College have a fleur-de-lis and lion for their royal founder, Henry VI, and three lilies to show the school's dedication to the Virgin Mary.

Pub sign

"My son... my eldest son"

Head of the family now

A large variety of animals were used too. If you concentrated on these you could collect a sizeable 'zoo' with no trouble at all. Pigeons, lions, unicorns – you name it and you will probably find it sooner or later.

As previously mentioned, only one man at a time could use a particular coat-of-arms; his sons had to add something to the family arms to 'make a difference', as it is called. Should you see a white stripe with tabs (or 'label') this shows that the owner is the eldest son, and that his father is still alive.

When the father died, the son would inherit his coat-of-arms along with any property. Off would come his 'label', to show that he was now the head of his family. Any sister could use the family arms without any difference, but on a diamond shape, not a shield. When she married she would add these arms to those of her husband, so a shield showing two sets side-by-side was that of a married couple. A shield divided into quarters arose when a wife had no brothers, and so inherited her father's arms herself – in this arrangement, her children were allowed to use them both. If this happened several times in a family's history then the coat-of-arms could become so complicated that no shield could hold it and a carpet would be needed! When things got to this stage, usually a selection of the most important quarters were chosen, otherwise everything would be too small to see properly.

If you like history, and are also interested in heraldry, you could well combine these two interests by looking into the Royal Coat-of-Arms. This has changed down the ages with the different monarchs and reflects the history of our country.

Heraldry is still very much

alive today, although it has strong links with the past. Investigate what lies behind your school badge, your Guide County badge, and later on your council's coat-of-arms, and you will find your own personal link with that past. Good hunting!

'*Learn about Heraldry*' in the Ladybird series tells you more of the history and rules of heraldry. The *Observer Book of Heraldry* goes into greater detail. Try this one later on, once you have acquired a basic knowledge of the subject.

Eton College

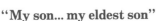

Eton College

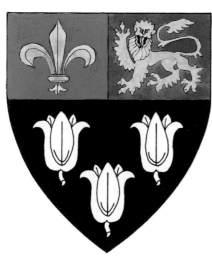

School badge

The making of Make-Up

by Fiona Lawson

Photographs by Chris Sheridan

Walk into any chemist's shop and you'll find that most of the shelf space is taken up by – not cameras, or medicines, or any of the other things you can buy in a chemist's – but cosmetics! Rows and rows of bottles and jars, pots and sticks. Eyeshadows, lipsticks, blushers, shaders, mascaras and nail-polish – all available in practically every shade under the sun.

You may not be wearing much make-up yet, but nevertheless, from the mid-teens onwards, most women wear at least lipstick or mascara every day. We apply it in the morning, perhaps touch it up during the day, and (hopefully!) remove it before bed. But have you ever stopped to think what goes into that little tube of lipstick before it reaches someone's make-up bag?

I decided to find out . . . so I went along to Miners Make-Up Ltd to find out just what does go into the making of make-up!

I was welcomed to the works complex by Dr. Fred Julietti, Special Services Manager for Miners. He explained that he would take me on a guided tour of the laboratories so that I could see exactly how cosmetics are put together. I put on a white lab coat

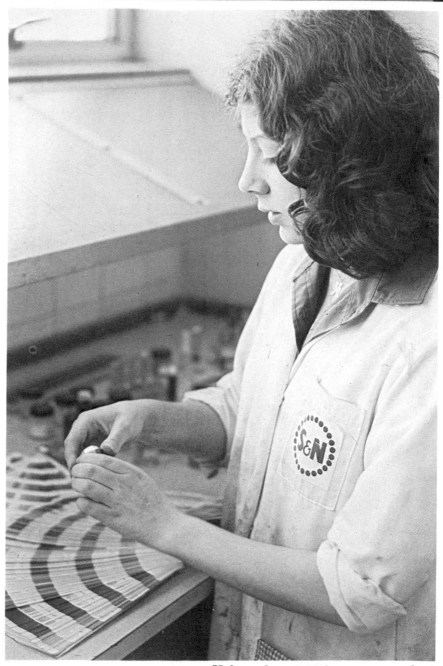

Helen colour-matches a new product.

to protect my clothes, grabbed my notepad and, feeling a little like a television doctor, followed Dr. Julietti round the laboratory.

Where does it all start, I asked? Who decides that a new lipstick or blusher should land on the chemist's shelves? I was told that Miners, in common with most cosmetics manufacturers, bring out a complete new range of make-up every few months – often this is to suit a new season – warm browns and reds for autumn, bright pastel shades for Spring, for example; or a new range can be brought out to complement a current fashion 'look', such as the 60s revival which was so popular last year. It is the role of Miners Creative Design Studio to keep in touch with current trends and even to try to predict what will be fashionable *next* season, so that Miners will have a make-up range to match.

Once the theme has been decided upon, the Creative Design Studio send a detailed 'briefing' to the laboratory. This lists the items to be included in the range – for example, six eyeshadows, four lipsticks with matching nail polish – and includes samples of the suggested colours. The laboratory staff are used to receiving all sorts of strange items as colour samples – bottle tops, leaves, someone's scarf – and being told to "match that"!

New products are always made up in small batches to start with, as a great deal of work still has to be done before the item is ready to be made up on a large scale.

Most items have one standard ingredient, to which colouring and specific other 'ingredients' are added to make the end product, and ultimately 'the look' which is uniquely Miners.

Helen Newton, a young Colour Technician in her second year of training, showed me some of the ingredients which go into the products.

Lipstick is based on wax, mascara on resins, and powder

A young technician feeds information into the lab equipment.

eyeshadows on talcum powder. Although 'pearl' effect eyeshadows are usually made up from synthetic products, I was fascinated to learn the best 'glittery' effect is produced by the addition of fish scales to the mixture! Evidently herring is the best 'sparkler' of all but, being expensive, other fish are used more often.

Colour experiments are also carried out at this stage, with some surprising results. Although black colouring added to foundation cream darkens it considerably, as you might expect, it has quite the opposite effect when added to a glossy lipstick. In fact, black pigment is

often used to *lighten* lipstick!

As Miners Make-Up is sold all over the world and not just in Britain, colours sometimes have to be altered to suit the specifications of different countries. America, for example, is keen on bright, vivid shades, while the Japanese prefer their make-up more subdued in tone!

Helen told me that after the first very small samples are made up and checked by the Design Studio for accuracy, etc., larger batches are then mixed in the laboratory for testing purposes. Miners have a 'test panel' of 3,000 young women who are regularly sent samples of products to try out in their own homes. They then

Perfumes are just as complicated to put together as cosmetics!

send in their comments on the products and only if a large majority of them like the product does work on it go ahead.

Every single batch of a product produced by Miners is carefully checked at every stage of its development. Some very complicated equipment is used in this area to ensure that not even one extra drop of, for example, apparently harmless palm oil, could sneak into a mixture and alter the formula!

Tiny amounts of mixture are tested on special machines to check that there are no 'alien' ingredients. Dr. Julietti proudly showed me the ultra-violet and infra-red 'spectrophotometers' which show precise details of a product's ingredients on graph paper. He also showed me a set of scales which can weigh in 1/10 millionths of a gram accurately and can weigh a human hair with great accuracy!

Tests are also continuously carried out to prevent any possibility of germs getting into the formula. Everywhere in the Lab, as I wandered around, I saw bottles and jars half full of liquids and creams, carefully being monitored for any signs of

These bags will all end up as lipsticks sooner or later!

bacteria, or other problems.

Once a product has been given the 'go ahead' for ingredients, it then undergoes a whole new set of tests to show that it can do its job! I was fascinated to see the equipment for testing the lasting power of nail polish, the softness of an eye pencil, and the percentage of glossiness in a lipstick! I was amused to learn however, that despite all this modern technology, the best way to test the 'smudgeability' of a mascara, according to Dr. Julietti, is to coat a false eyelash

with mascara, leave for a few moments, and then press it between two sheets of blotting paper!

Dr. Julietti then showd me how larger quantities of make-up are mixed up. As you might expect, the principle is very similar to that of an electric food mixer!

He explained, however, that the machines are in fact a bit more complicated than the average kitchen mixer! They are steam heated and water cooled, and make a very thorough job indeed of mixing up the product.

This ultra-modern scale weighs in 1/10 millionths of a gram!

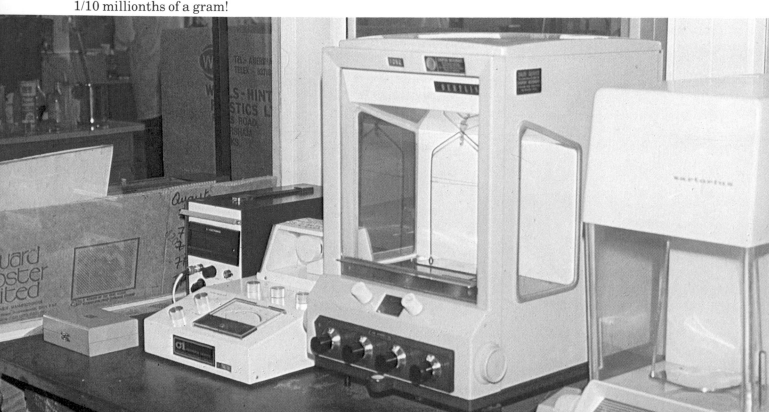

Firstly they grind down all the ingredients until they are as fine as possible, then giant blades stir them around until they are completely blended together. This can take some considerable time, as often there are conflicting ingredients involved which simply don't want to mix – such as oil and water – so the machines have to work extra hard to make sure that eventually they *do* blend. The water coolers are necessary to ensure that the high degree of heat does not discolour the product. The whole machine is vacuum sealed to prevent any

One of the lab's giant mixers.

air getting into the mixture and puffing it up.

When Dr. Julietti turned on one of the electric mixers to let me see it 'in action', I realised at once why he was wearing earphones! The high-pitched roar of the machinery can be quite deafening after a while, so the machine-minders are issued with special earphones which cut out high frequency noises but allow low-pitched human speech to be heard. He certainly seemed to be happily oblivious to the machinery noise when we photographed him!

Only when everything is absolutely satisfactory on all

counts does Dr. Julietti give the final go-ahead for the product to be produced on a large scale. Even then, the checking goes on – and on . . . Each batch has to match the previous one *precisely*, or it is not accepted.

At the same time, lots of work is going on elsewhere to ensure that the finished items on the chemist's shelves will look as good as possible. The Design Studio will have been working on the packaging for the range.

At the same time, the advertising section is busy thinking up catchy slogans and taking terrific photographs which bring the range to the attention of the public.

And finally – the finished products. Who would have believed that so much work could go on before you buy a lipstick?

Our grateful thanks to Dr. Julietti and to Mrs Marian Richards, Press Officer for Miners Make-Up, for their help with this feature.

P.S. If you are interested in becoming a Trainee Colour Technician in a cosmetics laboratory, like Helen, the best way to learn about the subject is actually 'on the job'. No particular

Dr. Julietti seems oblivious to the noisy machinery!

O or A levels are normally needed, just commonsense and a genuine interest in the job. Many cosmetic firms are listed in the Yellow Pages.

The finished products!

WORKING FOR A BETTER BRITAIN

by Brenda Apsley

The young people pictured here are doing something very useful, something that will benefit Britain in years to come. They aren't working as a punishment, they aren't being paid for their work, yet they are prepared to give up their valuable free time to do it. Why? Because they want to see a better environment around them – a better Britain – and they've decided to do something practical towards that aim.

Some years ago pupils and teachers from Greenhall High School near Edinburgh were visiting Mellon Udrigle in North-west Scotland when they noticed a change in the landscape. The marram-grassed sand dunes were suffering seriously from erosion, caused by a combination of wind, rain and sheep. The wide sandy area was slowly becoming bleak and featureless.

They decided that they wouldn't just sit back and watch the decline of the area – they went into action to combat the erosion. Teacher Douglas Hewat organised groups of pupils who, over the years, have brought about an impressive change in the landscape of Mellon Udrigle. In their spare time they have constructed brushwood fences to encourage the formation of new sand dunes, they have replanted the sands with tough new marram grass and turf, and they have even changed the course of a small stream – all in a practical attempt at reversing the natural decline in the area. And their efforts have paid off – they can *see* the success their hard work has achieved. Now Mellon Udrigle is a beautiful area once again – and it isn't only the pupils of Greenhall who now enjoy this wild corner of Scotland.

In fact, the pupils of Greenhall High School won an award for their project in the Shell Better Britain Competition. Shell, the Nature Conservancy Council and the Civic Trust are co-sponsors of the competition, which is designed to encourage young people not only to *think* about the environment, but also to take practical action to improve it.

All over Britain groups of young people from schools, societies and clubs are getting together to restore, maintain and improve their local environment – for everyone's benefit.

The Shell Better Britain Competition celebrates its twelfth anniversary in 1982, and since its instigation more than 25,000 people have taken part, organising hundreds of projects. They have two things in common – they care about the environment, and are prepared to work to improve it.

When the competition started, the emphasis was very much on rural nature conservation, but in recent years many inner-city community projects have also been undertaken.

And the projects aren't short-term commitments – many, like the Mellon Udrigle project, have been going on for some years, and will continue for many years to come. Conservation and environmental improvement demand continuing care if they are to be maintained, and the competition fosters that. The prizes that are awarded for the best projects are not given as a reward for the best work done, but as a means of continuing the projects.

What is common to the many projects which have been attempted over the years is the hard work and effort put in by the young people. As Hazel Barbour of Shell comments: "They are virtually unstoppable!"

If you would like more information about the Better Britain competition, write to: The Press Officer, Shell UK Ltd, Shell Mex House, Strand, London WC2. The competition is open to groups of children and young people up to the age of 22.

THE
AND

"Someone has taken my new red pencil!" shouted Victoria.

Lynne Grey, who was her Patrol Leader, sighed. "Trouble again," she thought.

Every Friday Victoria managed to upset the other Guides. Sometimes she spoiled the whole meeting for everyone. It hurt Lynne most of all, because everyone had started to complain about the Kingfishers, and they had been the best Patrol before Victoria joined. Lynne had tried and tried to be kind and helpful to the new girl, but this only seemed to make her worse.

"Someone's taken my pencil!" repeated Victoria, more loudly than before.

Lynne could see it on the floor, but before she could say so, Victoria had grabbed Lisa's pencil. They struggled until Lisa managed to get it back. Then Victoria began to rub her arm.

"Captain," she whined, "Lisa pushed me."

"Well, she made a line right across my picture," said Lisa indignantly, "and it was my best one ever."

"I expect *you* started it, Victoria," remarked the Captain, coming across to them. "You usually do. It's time you grew up a little and remembered that you are a Guide now, I think."

Victoria wasn't sorry. She didn't reply, and made a face when Miss Lucas turned away.

"It would serve you right if she turned you out of the Guides," Lisa told her.

"I wish she would," muttered one of the others.

Victoria tossed her head. "I don't care," she retorted.

She didn't seem to: during the rest of the evening she managed to knock a chair over twice and push Lynne down during a game. Then at hometime she rushed straight off without saying goodnight to anyone.

"I wish she'd never moved to our town," said Lisa as she tidied up. "She just doesn't fit in at all."

After the meeting, Lynne promised to drop in at her grandmother's to collect a parcel, and it was quite late before she set off home. As she hurried past Victoria's house – which stood by itself at the edge of a field – she was surprised to see Victoria herself leaning against the gate. It was rather dark and beginning to get chilly, yet she was still in her uniform without a cardigan.

"Lynne," she called in a shaky voice, "can you help me? I'm so frightened."

Lynne would have liked to walk on, but Victoria sounded really scared. So she stopped.

"What's wrong?" she asked.

"Mum is out . . . and there's a fierce cat in our porch that won't let me in."

KINGFISHER THE CAT

by Mary Cooper

Illustrated by
Valerie Sangster

Lynne loved cats and thought it was silly to be afraid of one, but she was too kind-hearted to smile.

"I'll come in with you," she said.

She walked boldly up the path and peered in through the porch window. There, in the most shadowy corner, crouched a big tabby cat with golden eyes.

"Hello, puss," she said gently, "may we come in?"

The reply set her heart pounding and made her jump back. A paw lashed out, with razor claws extended, and there came a most ferocious snarl.

The girls caught hold of each other, trembling.

"Oh Lynne, whatever shall we do?" whispered Victoria.

Lynne linked arms with her.

"You must come home with me," she answered. "Mum will let you wait in the warm, and Dad will be home by now. He will know what to do about the cat."

As they walked along the lane, Victoria began to cry.

"I hate it here," she said fiercely. "It's so lonely and creepy at night and Mum is always late back. She hates it too."

"Why did you come then?" asked Lynne.

Victoria rubbed her eyes hard with her handkerchief.

"We came because it's near to the hospital where Dad is. He is going to be there for a long time and Mum goes to see him every evening. That is what makes her late home."

She gave a sniff, then walked on in silence. After a minute she turned to Lynne with a frown.

"You needn't think I'm going to like you because you're helping me," she muttered angrily.

Lynne tightened her lips and said nothing until they were home and mother had opened the door.

"I've brought Victoria," she explained, and told her what had happened.

Mrs Grey had heard all about Victoria, but she welcomed her in like a friend.

"Come in and sit down. You must be frozen," she said.

Mr Grey had listened to their story too. He went to the corner cupboard and took out his heavy motor-cycling gloves.

"These should stop me from getting scratched," he remarked. "Wait here until I see what can be done."

He hurried away down the lane and was gone some time. When he came back, Lynne and Victoria were sitting at the kitchen table with steaming cups of cocoa in front of them and Victoria was chattering quite happily to Mrs Grey. They all looked up expectantly as he opened the back door.

"I've put him in the outhouse," he told them. "It took some doing to catch him, but I managed it in the end." He turned to his wife. "You'll never guess who it is," he added, "Mrs Mason's Benny, come back after all this time."

"Poor thing!" said Mother. "He must have thought his mistress had come home again."

Mrs Mason had owned the cottage where Victoria lived now. On the day she had left for Australia her cat had run away, and although everyone searched and searched, he hadn't been seen again. The house had been empty for almost a year, so everyone thought he had gone for good.

"He must have had a hard time of it," said Mr Grey. "He has gone quite wild."

"Will we be able to keep him?" asked Lynne.

"That depends on whether he wants to stay," answered her mother. "In any case, it will take a great deal of kindness to tame him . . . and patience too."

"How much?" Lynne looked anxious, and her mother smiled.

"As much as you think you can possibly give . . . and then some more," she replied. Then she turned to Victoria.

"Would you like to come and help with him?"

Victoria looked at the floor and didn't answer at once. Then she lifted her head.

"I don't mind if Lynne doesn't," she said, gruffly.

During the next week she came with Lynne every evening and together they put down a saucer of food.

Benny hid in the corner and wouldn't eat until they had gone . . . but he didn't snarl at them.

The next Friday Victoria was cheerful and well-behaved for almost the whole of the time at Guides.

The following week Benny came out for his supper as soon as they put it down.

On the Guide outing to Hornbeam Woods Victoria stayed with Lynne all the time and didn't make any trouble at all. She had tea with Lynne afterwards and Benny came into the kitchen to see them.

Three weeks later, the Kingfishers won the gold cup for being the best Patrol. That same evening, Victoria came running up in great excitement.

"Dad's coming out of hospital tomorrow!" she cried.

"That's wonderful," said Mrs Grey. "Come and tell us all about it."

Victoria sat on the sofa, where Benny was curled in a big fluffy ball. When he felt her beside him, he opened his beautiful golden eyes and began to purr.

Mrs Grey smiled. The girl and the cat – both strange and frightened – but kindness had won them over!

ARE YOU FIT FOR ANYTHING?

devised by Fiona Lawson
Illustrated by Debbie Clarke

"A healthy mind means a healthy body" runs the old saying. Well, *we* think it should be the other way around – because if your body is fit and active, and giving you no cause for concern, you can occupy your mind with all the things you want to do, and get on with enjoying life. Try our quiz on your friends – the answers may surprise you, too!

Start off by answering these statements as true or false:

1. An apple cleans your teeth as well as a toothbrush does. True or false? *False*

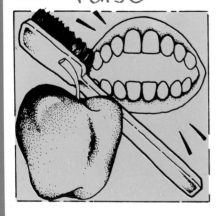

2. Brown bread is always better for you than white. True or false? *False*

3. High heels can cause permanent damage to the feet. True or false? *True*

4. White rice is more digestible than brown rice. True or false?

5. A hot bath just after a meal can be dangerous. True or false? *True*

6. Sugar gives you energy. True or false? *True*

7. 'Puppy fat' will disappear of its own accord. True or false? *False*

8. A bowl of muesli is a more balanced meal than steak and kidney pie, peas and roast potatoes. True or false? *True*

9. The hair on your head is already dead. True or false? *True*

10. If you pull out one grey hair six more will grow in its place. True or false? *False*

Now work through these questions, answering a, b or c for each one.

1. Nails should be filed:
   √ a. from the sides to the centre
   b. from the centre out
   c. in a see-saw fashion

2. Which has most calories:
   a. a slice of bread
   √ b. ½ oz of butter
   c. 3 potatoes

3. Hair should be trimmed:
   a. once a week
   √ b. every six weeks
   c. every six months

4. Which is the best all-round exercise:
   a. walking
   b. rowing
   √ c. swimming

5. Vitamin D is absorbed through the skin from:
   √ a. the sun
   b. the moon
   c. the sea

6. Gelatine is good for the:
   a. skin
   b. hair
   √ c. nails

7. A good conditioner for dry hair is:
   a. baby oil
   b. cod liver oil
   √ c. olive oil

8. A can of fizzy drink has how many calories:
   a. 25
   b. 85
   ✓ c. 140

9. Which of these are most people not eating enough of:
   a. protein
   b. carbohydrates
   ✓ c. roughage

10. Under-arm deodorants should be used:
    a. every day, instead of washing
    ✓ b. every day, after washing
    c. once a week

11. In winter, lips should be protected from the wind with:
    a. moisturiser
    b. orange juice
    ✓ c. lip salve

12. Eyebrow hair should be removed with:
    ✓ a. tweezers
    b. a razor
    c. scissors

13. Which of the following can the body do without:
    a. water
    b. protein
    c. fats   None

14. Toothbrushes should be replaced:
    ✓ a. once a month
    b. once every two months
    c. once every six months

15. Cycling is a good way of trimming the:
    ✓ a. thighs
    b. calves
    c. stomach

16. Which of these contain sugar:
    ✓ a. tinned soup
    ✓ b. tinned beef stew
    ✓ c. tinned fruit

17. The best way to help clear a spotty skin is to:
    ✓ a. keep it scrupulously clean
    ✓ b. stop eating chocolate
    c. dab it with lemon juice

18. A dash of vinegar in the rinsing water is good for:
    a. dry hair
    b. fair hair
    ✓ c. greasy hair

19. Which of these contain artificial colouring:
    ✓ a. tinned peas
    ✓ b. vanilla ice cream (shop bought)
    c. brand name jam

20. How much exercise should we take each day (including walking etc.):
    a. 2 minutes
    ✓ b. 1 hour
    c. 6 hours

21. Which of these preparations is good for the skin:
    a. talc
    ✓ b. bath oil
    c. bubble bath

22. Teeth will look whiter and brighter for an occasional brushing with:
    a. milk
    ✓ b. salt
    c. soot

23. Most teenagers need how many hours sleep a night:
    a. four
    ✓ b. eight
    c. ten

24. Which is the best for your skin in the morning:
    ✓ a. cold water
    b. skin freshener
    c. cold tea

25. A good tip for nail biters is to:
    a. dip the nails in washing up liquid twice a day
    b. wear rubber gloves all the time
    ✓ c. paint the nails with clear nail polish.

Now turn to page 61 for the answers!

CRAZY CURIOSITIES

by Fiona Lawson
Illustrated by Lynn Breeze

We all know that a black cat crossing our path is meant to bring good luck, but did you know that animal superstitions don't just stop at cats? Far from it! So, just for fun, we've compiled a list of the more unusual ones – definitely *not* to be taken too seriously!

If you meet a toothless BADGER you'll know that at least one old superstition hasn't died out yet – that of keeping a badger's tooth in your pocket at all times to ensure that you will win any bets you might make!

An old French belief holds that keeping a BAT's eye in the pocket will make the owner invisible (not to mention unpopular . . .)

Farmers still have some quaint old customs which they carry out to this day, one of the most interesting being that giving a piece of mistletoe to the first CALF born in the New Year will ensure good luck and happiness for the whole family throughout the coming year. It's not known whether they also have to kiss the calf under the mistletoe!

Yorkshire folk used to maintain that they could bring themselves good luck by tossing a hairy CATERPILLAR over the left shoulder. Not so lucky for whoever it landed on, maybe?

America used to have what must be one of the silliest superstitions of all – that drinking a concoction of crushed and boiled CRICKETS would give a lovely singing voice. UGH!

In Germany it used to be said that lumbago sufferers would magically be cured if they went outside and rolled on the grass as soon as they heard the first CUCKOO of the year!

The expression 'hair of the dog that bit you' actually had nothing to do with hangovers in olden days. It originated from the idea that the only way to cure the bite of a mad DOG was to capture the dog, pull out a few of its hairs, and eat them with a piece of bread. Could this be a shaggy dog story?

Did you know that people used to believe that the only way to cure measles was to take a ride on a DONKEY – facing backwards? Well, it would certainly take your mind off your measles!

In olden times in Germany it was believed that a FLEA bite on the hand meant either that the recipient was going to be kissed, or that they were going to receive some good news.

A charming old English country rhyme relates to eating GOOSE meat on Michaelmas Day, September 29th:

Whosoever eats goose on
Michaelmas Day,
Shall never lack money his
debts to pay.

In certain parts of South America, until the last century, it was believed that a sick person could be cured by taking a GOAT into the garden of the house where the sick person lay, and letting it eat its fill of the grass there. The goat would then wander off, taking the illness away with it from the house.

There is a particularly nice little story attached to LADYBIRDS. If you count the spots on the back of a ladybird which has alighted on you, you will have a month of good luck for each one of the spots.

The paw of that pretty little creature, the MOLE, was once believed to be excellent for curing toothache if kept in the pocket. Can't be much fun for the mole, though!

Fishermen in Scotland think that if the word PIG is mentioned on board the vessel, there will be a poor catch. Of fish, or of pigs?

If you go out at dawn on May Day, find a SNAIL, and put it on a hearth which still has wood ash on it from the night before; its trail will form the initial of your true love. There must be easier ways ...

SPIDERS aren't exactly favourite household pets in this country, but you might well feel a bit happier about them if you lived in France and saw one after lunchtime, according to the old rhyme:

Araignée du matin, chagrin;
Araignée du tantôt, cadeau;
Araignée du soir, espoir.

(See a spider in the morning – sorrow, in the afternoon – a gift; in the evening – hope.)

There is a long held belief in rural England that if a TOAD crosses a bride's path on her way to the wedding, she and her husband will have a long and prosperous life together.

In certain countries in Europe the people still insist that it is absolutely impossible for a human being to catch a WEASEL asleep (but are they referring to the human being or the weasel?)

For many years Canadian wives of WHALE fishermen had to stay in bed and refuse all food while their husbands were at sea, or the men would not have a good catch.

In France, mothers used to tell their children never to touch a WREN'S nest, or they would surely break a bone the same day!

ON THE AIR!

The Isle of Man Girl Guides celebrated Thinking Day in a rather unusual and *very* enterprising way ...

As the Isle of Man had just completed its Millenium celebrations, the Guide Commissioner for the Island decided that Thinking Day ought to be equally memorable.

After much discussion, the idea was born to do a five-minute spot each day for a week on the local Manx Radio, ending on Thinking Day. Brownies, Guides and Rangers were each asked to devise their own scripts on the theme of "What does the Promise mean to me?" A committee of four Guiders and the Island Commissioner planned the order of the programmes, and the week started with a short talk by the International Adviser, Mrs. Kelly. She was followed by four of the 1st Castletown Brownies. Then came the Kingfisher Patrol of the 1st Braddan Guides and the Douglas and Southern Rangers. Two Rangers were to be invested during the course of their programme. Then followed the Island's handicapped Company, Cronk Gennal (which, incidentally, means Happy Place) and after them one of the oldest

members of the Trefoil Guild chatted with the Island Commissioner. The only time the broadcast could go out was 10.30 a.m., so everything had to be pre-recorded.

On a very wet and windy February night, all concerned gathered at the recording studio – excited Brownies, apprehensive Guides and decidedly nervous Rangers – but they need not have worried, as a very pleasant and helpful engineer soon put them at their ease, and proceeded to get the very best out of them all. The evening ended in a very unexpected way, as one of the disc jockeys was doing a live broadcast in the next studio and interviewed some of the girls on the air, later playing many of their requests. Everyone agreed that it had been a memorable way of marking Thinking Day for all the Island units. The broadcasts made quite a talking point among the community, being not only a worthwhile project but also a good public relations exercise.

The Kingfisher Patrol about to become radio stars!

The Kingfisher Patrol of the 1st Braddan Guides talk about their visit to Manx Radio in their own words:

"It all started when our Guider, Mrs. MacDonal, said that there was to be a competition for the best three-minute speech on the theme of Thinking Day, and that we had three weeks in which to write it. Our Island Commissioner, Mrs. Corrin, came to the meeting to hear our speeches and decided that our Patrol's was the best one.

"So, on February 14th at 6.30 p.m., we met outside Manx Radio. The door into the station was, surprisingly, only a little wooden door. We were taken to a waiting room where we sat for about half an hour, getting more and more nervous, and were then taken to 'Studio B'. We gathered around the microphones and spoke into them so that the engineers could get used to our voices. We managed to get our part of the broadcast recorded with only two mistakes!

"Our speech mentioned that the Guide Movement was universal, and that if we tried we could do 365 good turns in a year and 366 in a leap year.

"After the recording session, we went round the radio station and talked to one of the disc jockeys who was on the air."

The Isle of Man Guides certainly had a good idea when they thought of publicising themselves on local radio. Why

not approach *your* local radio station to find out if they can give you a little of their valuable air time? Be prepared to accept an 'offpeak' listening hour, such as late at night or early in the morning, and for the time given to be very short indeed, depending on how much 'spare time' the station has available.

Although the programme itself will almost definitely be pre-recorded, you will need to do lots of preparatory work beforehand if you want to sound at all professional 'on the air'. The radio station staff will give you

The Douglas and Southern Rangers seem to have overcome their initial nerves!

valuable assistance, but they are busy people and you must not expect them to prepare the programme entirely for you.

If you are seriously thinking of putting yourselves on the air, try to have the idea for your programme roughed out before you approach the radio station. Your idea will stand a much better chance of being accepted if you seem to know what you are doing!

Quite apart from being well thought out, though, the programme must *appeal* to the public. The last thing the radio producer wants is for the listeners to switch off or, worse, change to another station!

Local radio reaches thousands of people. Could it help you to get the Guiding message across?

Nature at Night

Ann Pinder tells you about some of the countryside sights and sounds to watch out for on a night hike.

At night things might *seem* quiet, with few cars on the roads, and most people tucked up in bed . . . but don't be misled! The darkness is only a camouflaging coat which masks the activities of a wealth of wildlife.

That scuffling in the hedgerow, for instance, may well announce the arrival of the hedgehog, shuffling along in search of beetles and slugs, snuffling and snorting as he feeds. No wonder country people call him the hedge-pig, though unlike his farmyard namesake, he hides beneath a hedge during the day and only emerges at dusk to go in search of food. Sadly, many a hedgehog meets his end while crossing the road at night, for on the approach of a vehicle the animal stops, then rolls into a prickly ball. It's a protective measure that simply doesn't work with cars, and it will be interesting to discover if, in years to come, hedgehogs begin to learn about these powerful enemies, so that they can take more successful defensive action, such as a quick dash for the safety of the grass verge.

Badgers live in a maze of underground tunnels whose entrances may be discovered in sandy banks. It's easy to tell if anyone is at home, for during the half-light of dusk or dawn the warmth of the occupants' breath may soon be issuing out as steam. Footprints may be observed in the soft soil in front of the *sett*, and look here too for strands of bracken, sure evidence that Brock the badger has been bringing in clean bedding, trundling backwards through the undergrowth with his pile of 'clean sheets' held between chin and front paws.

The fox's presence is marked very much by smell. Not only does the animal mark its territory by emitting a strong scent from a gland beneath the tail, he also leaves food remains rotting in the earth. A sore trial Reynard must be to his fastidious badger neighbours!

Some foxes have become emboldened in recent years to move into the suburbs. By day, they hide up, for instance, in holes excavated beneath the garden sheds, and at night forage in the dustbins for food, becoming a familiar sight to residents, who sometimes see them trotting down the lighted streets with all the assurance of pet dogs.

Listen out for the bark of the dog fox, a sharp yelp repeated several times, and for the screeching reply of the vixen. Listen, too, for the calls of the night birds, the tuneful trill of the nightingale, and the churring note of the nightjar, which by day, perches along, and not across, branches, being so well camouflaged that it looks just like part of the tree.

The familiar *twit-to-woo* marks the presence of a pair of Tawny Owls calling to each other, while a bloodcurdling screech heralds the so-called 'ghost owl', the heart-faced Barn Owl which, with its eerie call and white plumage has caused many a person at night to think they had heard a supernatural spook!

The owl is ideally suited to the dark, for not only does it have excellent vision, but also hearing so acute that the smallest rustle in the grass can be heard. In addition, the owl's wing feathers have specially softened edges, so that it can swoop down silently and takes its prey by surprise.

We can tell exactly what owls eat by examining their pellets – capsules of bone, fur and feather which are regurgitated because these parts cannot be digested by the bird. In pellets are found the remains of insects, plants, birds and small rodents such as voles and mice, which frequent the hedgerows in order to sample berries and nuts. Their squeaks may be heard coming from the hedgerow or from the long grass bordering the fields: very much a *dead* giveaway if an owl or one of the 'tigers' of the hedgerow – a stoat or weasel – is about.

One squeak unlikely to be heard however, is that of the bat. For centuries man has regarded this creature with suspicion, for not only was it black, a colour associated with evil, but it did everything the wrong way round – coming out at night, and hanging upside-down. The bat's diabolical reputation has been enhanced by one South American species – the Vampire Bat – which lives on blood, but fortunately British bats prefer a diet of insects.

Bats do not have to be keen-sighted, for they communicate with each other by a form of navigation called *echo location*. This means that squeaks made by the bat bounce off surrounding objects, enabling it to ascertain not only the whereabouts of an obstacle, but also its size. Generally, human adults cannot hear a bat squeak, as the sound is too high-pitched, but children and young people can sometimes hear some of the lower bat frequencies.

Moths are on the bat menu. On your night walk, take a good sniff at the scents of the night, for many of these are designed to attract the attention of moths, coming as they do from flowers like night-scented stock, honeysuckle and the Evening Primrose, a tall plant with yellow tubular flowers which grows on grassy banks. Not only do such blooms attract moths by scent, but their pale, luminescent colours are designed to show up in the dark.

Moths, then, work by scent as well as by sight, just like many of the larger nocturnal animals, who use hearing, scent and sight, as well as stealth and alertness, in order to catch their food, or avoid being caught themselves. They use all the senses – a lesson we would do well to emulate if we want to observe nature at night.

Illustrated by Bob Hersey

THE FOUR WORLD CENTRES

Did you know that the World Association of Girl Guides and Girl Scouts (W.A.G.G.G.S.) owns four different centres in four quite different parts of the world? They are open to every member of the Movement over fourteen, and everyone is made equally welcome, from parties of young Guides on holiday to Commissioners attending an important World Guiding Conference.

Illustrated by Kate Lloyd-Jones

1. This is 'Our Chalet', at Adelboden in Switzerland. It opened in 1932 and was built entirely thanks to the generosity of Mrs. Storrow, then Chairman of the World Committee. It is ideally situated for whizzing down the surrounding ski slopes, going for long, energetic hikes, or simply sitting peacefully amid the flowers and the fir trees, lazily enjoying the view!

2. 'Olave House' is in central London, conveniently situated near Earl's Court underground station, and an ideal base for shopping and sightseeing in the Capital. The centre has had several locations in London, finally moving to the Earl's Court premises in 1959. Originally called 'Our Ark', the name was later changed to Olave House in 1963 in honour of the Chief Guide.

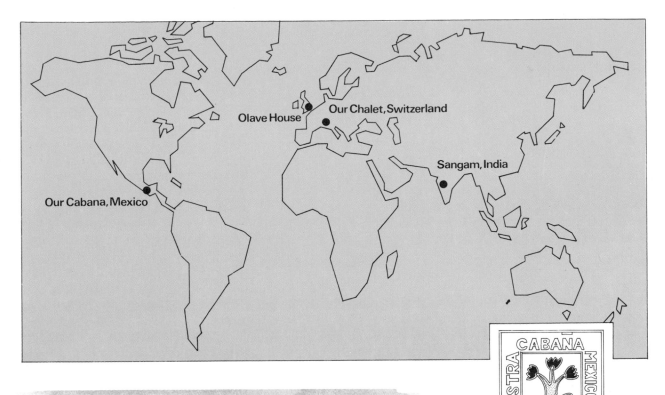

3. In the early 1950s, seeing how successful Our Chalet had become, it was decided that another centre should be opened, this time in South America. A generous donation from the Girl Scouts of the U.S.A. paid for five acres of land at Cuernavaca, near Mexico City. 'Our Cabana' was officially opened in 1957, and since then thousands of Guides and Guiders have visited this beautiful area, famous for its crafts, including weaving and silver work.

4. At the eighteenth World Conference in 1963 it was decided that the next centre should be at Poona, in India, and that it should be named *Sangam*, a Hindu word meaning 'going together'. The foundation stone was laid in 1964 and two years later Sangam celebrated its first Thinking Day. Its long, low buildings, grassed areas and swimming pool are set in beautiful surroundings, happily blessed with a better climate than most of India.

ALL SYSTEMS GO FOR THE BEWBUSH BUS!

The Supersonic Playbus. Doesn't it look great fun?

For over a year now, a number of young people have been involved in various community projects, under the auspices of the Girl Guides Association. As part of the Association's Silver Jubilee Project, groups of volunteers – mostly sixth formers and young unemployed people – have been trained to run projects in different parts of the country. Supported by grants from the Queen's Silver Jubilee Trust Fund and the Department of Education and Science, the intention of the scheme has been to encourage the

same kind of leadership from the volunteers as the Association gives to its members. The young people involved, by no means all Guides, have given a highly individual character to the schemes which have developed.

Training for the volunteers began in January 1980 at the G.G.A. Training Centre, Waddow Hall in Lancashire. They were plunged straightaway into an intensive five-day course in Community Leadership, covering playground activities, sessions on craft, music and street theatre,

and child psychology. The success of the course was evident in the enthusiasm and friendship it generated. Gradually, local communities became involved in the schemes, and the way was made clear for the volunteers to begin their real work.

In August last year, for example, the community of Bewbush, in Crawley, Sussex, took delivery of a double decker 'Fun Bus' for the children of the area. Crawley Borough Council could not afford to build a much-needed community centre,

so were delighted when the Girl Guides Association, in conjunction with British Caledonian Airways and The British Airports Authority, offered them the bus.

It had been bought, by the Guides, from Eastbourne Corporation, and has been completely stripped, refurbished and painted inside and out by British Caledonian workmen.

The 'Supersonic Bus', now used as a playcentre for the Bewbush under-fives, contains, among other things, a kitchen, bathroom and playhouse, and it is decorated outside in a brightly-coloured, cartoon-style aviation theme.

Although all the young people involved in running the Playbus Scheme have been given training and support by the G.G.A., the day-to-day arrangements and decisions have been entirely their own responsibility. Once the Association had helped set things in motion, the volunteers were encouraged to make what they wanted of everything.

Think about *your* area. Is there anything that badly needs to be done which you could help with? Bewbush now has a Playbus – what could *your* town have?

Two of the Bewbush children hand over framed 'thank you' letters

Photographs by Chris Sheridan.

You will need: 14 balls of double knitting wool in royal blue, plus 2 balls of double knitting wool in gold. Also: 1 pair of no. 9 (3¾ mm) needles and a large crochet hook for the fringe.

Measurements: The scarf will be roughly 8 ins wide by 84 ins long (excluding the fringe), depending on how tight your knitting is.

Tension guide: 11 stitches measure 2 ins.

Instructions: Cast on 46 stitches in blue. Knit 84 ins. Cast off.

Pockets: Cast on 29 stitches in gold. Work 5 ins. Cast off. Repeat for second pocket.

To make up the scarf: Press the knitting with a warm iron first. Now sew on the pockets 3 ins from the ends. Trim the ends of the scarf with 5 ins fringe in alternate strands of blue and gold. To do this you must loop equal lengths of yarn through the ends of the scarf with a crochet hook.

Winter Warmer!

Even if you've never knitted anything before, you can make up our two-colour scarf in no time, it's so easy! And your hands will be warm all winter! We've knitted our scarf up in Guide blue and gold, although of course it is *not* part of the Guide uniform. You can choose any colours you like – dark and light shades of green would be pretty, red and yellow would be fun on a cold winter's day!

Our scarf was knitted for us by Victoria Morrison.

58

WIN A DAY IN LONDON

Guides – Enter our exciting competition!

All you have to do is look carefully at these six photographs, and tell us what you think they are. They are all everyday objects, but taken from rather unusual angles!

Now, underneath your answers, tell us what you liked best about this year's Guide Annual, and why. That's all!

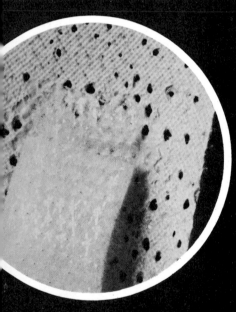

The first prize is an all-expenses paid trip to London for the winner and a relative, spending a day with the Editor of the Annual. It should be a very exciting day, with all sorts of treats laid on. (A cash alternative may be arranged, if necessary.) There will also be some super runner-up prizes, so put your thinking caps on now!

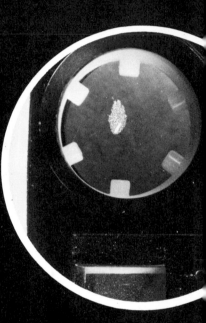

Send your entries to: The Editor, The Girl Guide Annual, 17-19 Buckingham Palace Road, London, SW1W 0PT. Don't forget to give your full name, address, age, and the name of your Guide Company. Fit it all on a postcard if you possibly can.

Closing date for entries is March 31st 1982. The winners will be notified by post, and the Editor's decision is final.

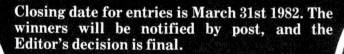

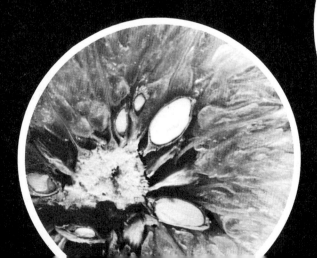

ANSWERS

NATURE CROSSWORD

```
        SLUG U
      S     E U
      E     A L
COAL        LOCH
R           A   A
O           R   R
WASP        MOLE
  A         O
  R         T
  RUSH
```

PROVERBS CROSSWORD

Across

1. Share 3. Half 7. One 8. Waters 10. Broth 12. Early 13. Pound 15. Acorns 18. Sun 19. Rich 20. Cloth

Down

2. Haste 3. Hungry 4. Fly 5. New 6. Bread 9. It's 10. Black 11. Rod 12. Enough 14. Fruit 16. Shy 17. War

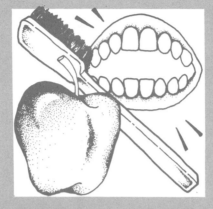

ARE YOU FIT FOR ANYTHING?

Health and beauty quiz

Give yourself one point for each correct answer and make a note of your score.

True or false section: 1. False. The fruit sugar can cause decay, so brush whenever possible. 2. False. Wholemeal bread is very good for you, but sliced brown bread is often just dyed white bread. 3. True. Don't wear them every day. 4. False. The husk on brown rice aids digestion. 5. True. You could fall asleep in the bath after all that food. 6. True. But remember that too much white sugar is bad for you – and your teeth! 7. False. Unfortunately, you have to help it away! 8. True. The latter meal contains far too many fats. 9. True. What you eat affects the hair still growing inside, though. 10. False. If you start worrying about grey hair, though, you will probably notice the odd ones more than you did before.

Questions: I. a. This helps to prevent splitting nails. 2. b. Watch those fats! 3. b. This is quite often enough to help

avoid split ends. 4. c. And it's fun! 5. a. Make the most of the summer out of doors. 6. c. Try a cube of table jelly a day. 7. c. Leave on for 10 mins., then wash hair normally with shampoo. 8. c. Horrifying! Remember too that most low calorie drinks contain saccharin, which some doctors believe to be bad for you. 9. c. Find it in fresh fruit and vegetables and wholemeal bread. 10. b. Every single day. 11. c. Vaseline makes a good substitute. 12. a. *Never* try anything else! 13. None of them! 14. a. if possible, or b. at the latest. Old brushes can miss parts of your teeth. 15. a. And it's free! 16. All of them. The manufacturers say we *prefer* the taste. 17. a. and b. Drinking lots of water is a good tip, too. 18. c. Helps prevent grease building up. 19. All of them – yes, even the peas! 20. b. Good for the body *and* the mind. 21. b. It softens the skin – the others have no real function. 22. b. Use toothpaste afterwards to remove the taste. Interestingly enough, there are also people who swear by soot! 23. b. Your body is growing and it needs a lot of rest. 24. a Not if you are prone to thread veins on the cheeks, however. 25. c. It will draw attention to your nails whenever you try to bite them absentmindedly.

Now add up your correct answers.

25 to 35 points – excellent, you could have written this quiz yourself! 15 to 25 – not bad, and you should have picked up a lot of information from the answers. 5 to 15 – try to take more interest in your appearance and health. It's definitely worth it. Under 5 – what are you, a gorilla?

Use ribbons narrow or wide, plain or patterned, satin or cotton or velvet, matching or contrasting, in a variety of ways to brighten up the dullest clothes!

Remember
by Jil Shipley

Sew military style V-shaped ribbons onto a khaki shirt.

Sew a couple of V-shapes to the back of the shirt as well.

Tie a pretty ribbon to a hair-grip. Wear several together!

Sew narrow satin ribbons in a fan-shape from shoulder to waist on a plain dress then tie the ribbons in a bow at the waist.

Sew diagonal stripes of narrow ribbon across a pocket and at the outside edge of a sleeve cuff.

Bind the edge of a collar and add stripes to a yoke with contrasting ribbon.

Remove the buttons and add bows! Sew onto each button position a 20cm. length of ribbon. Slot it through the buttonhole and tie a bow.

Put stripes of black ribbon across the pocket and down the leg of a pair of white trousers.

Sew shiny black buttons on the waist-band to match.

Make a nightie simply by sewing 180 cm. of pretty fabric into a tube, hemming the top and bottom edge, inserting elastic into the top hem and gathering it to fit your chest. Add ribbons to tie on your shoulders as straps.

180cm.

100cm.

Zig-zag a ribbon round the hem of a skirt. Do the corners like this.

Sew a band of ribbon round the hemline.

62